PENNY UNVEILED

The Penny Chronicles

Vol. 1

By: Penny Earvin

ACKNOWLEDGEMENTS

This book is dedicated to my children. First, I want to honor my Lord and Savior for giving me the strength to go on. You have carried me every step of the way. Even when I was at my lowest point, you brought me through.

Artis, thank you for loving me even when I don't deserve it. You have grown to be a great father, husband, friend, son. Just know I have always loved you from the time I felt you in my wound.

Dennisha, my first-born baby girl, thank you for being who you are. I grew and learned because of you. You mean the world to me, and I could not imagine my life without you. When you were little, I used to tell you that you were my little guinea pig, and every day, I learn from you. Thank you for teaching me how to be a mom. I love your Mommanish.

Dominique, words cannot express the love I have for you. You have grown to be a beautiful young woman inside and out. I wish to be more like you. Just know your love for me has not gone unnoticed. You are the glue that holds this family together. I'm so grateful to have you to call when I just need someone to talk to. Thank you for being my best friend. I love you Domo.

Zackary, thank you for keeping me grounded in your love. Not only to have a love for myself but for all my children. Thank you for your wisdom and knowledge. My world is worthless without you. You keep me on my toes. You are a lot like me, the middle child, strong and brave. You can conquer the world. I love you always even when you thought I didn't. I love you Wooga.

Sasha, baby girl, you know I love you to the moon and back. You are beautiful, and I am humbled and grateful to call you my daughter. You have grown to be a great mother, wife, friend. I smile when you are happy; I cry when you are sad. The world is yours; just reach up and grab it. I love you Sasha Cakes.

My baby boy, Marquis, thank you for listening even when you did not want to. I love you always. You are my everything. Stay strong son. You are my golden child; your smile and laughter when you are happy and sad help me to keep living. I love you baby boy.

To wrap it up in a nutshell, I want the world to know I could not have made it without my children. I may not have been the perfect mom, but just know you are loved, and I appreciate how you tell it like it is. I have always told my children to speak what is on their minds, even if it hurts. Well, you got that down to a science, lol. I appreciate how even though your childhood may not have been the best, you still find a way in your heart to love me anyway. And for that, I am grateful. Just know I have enjoyed every moment with you. I was able to live my childhood through you. Thank you for allowing me to be your mom. I was able to finish this book because of you.

I love you always,

Mom

CONTENTS

PRELUDE | I NEED COFFEE

I can't wait until I go to Las Vegas. Sure, I have been there several times, but this time is special. I will be meeting my sisters for the very first time. Plus, it's my birthday! I will be turning 50 this year. Half a century, and it has been a long time coming. As I press the send button for my final payment for a rental house, my heart begins to thump, a kind of thump that I have never felt before. Maybe it's my nerves. What will they think about me? Am I too dark? Too tall? Too fat?

The alarm goes off. It's 6 am, time to get up out of bed and start my day. I close my laptop and turn on the t.v watch the news. I like to look at the weather and to see if there are any traffic jams on the 385. There is always a jam my route to work. So annoying.

"Can I get a snack for my lunch," my granddaughter asks?

"Can you wait until I get dressed?" Irritated, I rush and put my clothes on, thinking, shit, I forgot I don't have my coffee. It is going to be a very long day. I always forget stuff when I don't have my meds, which is the caffeine that I so desperately need every day.

"Where is my snack Grandme?"

"Dammit, can you hold on?" I say under my breath.

Standing at my bedroom door is this long leg thin girl, all smiles. "Well, are you going to give me a snack for my lunch?" I look at her with disbelief, I am so blessed to have such a beautiful, smart grandchild, but her mouth is something else. She wants it when she wants it. Just like her mother.

"Can you give me one minute? Go let the dog out. Did you wash your face?"

"I forgot." Still standing at the door.

"Go and do like I said. I will be downstairs in a minute."

"Don't forget my snack," she says again.

"I know, little girl, just get ready; we only have 10 minutes left before we have to go to school."

Looking at myself in the full body mirror, I start to think back to when I was a little girl. Questions always ring in my head. Where did I get this color? Why do I have freckles on my face? Why am I different from anyone that I was raised around? Do I favor my mother? Who, by the way, will be coming to visit me next week for the first time.

I will soon find out. It's two months before the big trip to Vegas. They say what goes on in Vegas stays in Vegas but not this time.

"Grandme!"

"I'm coming!"

At the bottom of the stairs, Nicole is waiting patiently for her snack, daring not to say anything because she knows that the clock is ticking, and I am running around the kitchen angry because I yet do not have any coffee.

Nicole knows that look. You know the look that your mother gives you when they are saying something that only you and her know all too well. What am I going to eat for lunch? It's bad enough that I don't have any coffee. Looking at the time, damn, it's already time to go to work.

"Where are my keys?" asks my husband, standing 6 feet tall, slender and dark-skinned. "How am I supposed to know? Look in the door; you always leave your keys in the door. Nicole, let Sugar in and lock the door; it's time to go."

"Mom? My snack."

"Just find something in the pantry so we can go." Nicole rushes to the pantry and grabs a Capri Sun and some chips.

"Now we can go," smiled Nicole.

"Did you wash your face?"

"Yes, Grandme."

I grabbed my purse and keys.

"These are not my keys. Where are my keys?"

"David, your keys are on the table." I frantically start running around the room. "Where are my keys?"

"They are in the door," said my husband David, chuckling.

"Don't get funny with me; you probably put them there on purpose to throw me off. You know I have breakfast duty at school and there is a traffic jam on the 385." Outside in the cool breeze was my brand-new car. I push the unlock button and open the door. Yes, it still has that new car smell. "Put your seatbelt on," I told Nicole.

"OK Grandme. You know that we can stop at Krispy Kake and get coffee," Nicole says while glancing at me through the rearview mirror.

"Are you telling me this because you are such a sweet child, and you know I need coffee? Or are you telling me because you want that pink sprinkle donut?"

"Both," Nicole says, fastening her seat belt.

I look at her in the mirror and smile. I was thinking the same thing. Five more minutes would not hurt much.

9

Plus, I do not want to go postal on any student today without my caffeine. "That'll work for me," Nicole added, checking to make sure her seatbelt was tight.

Say no more; Krispy Kake it is. I thought to myself as I applied pressure to the gas pedal. We will be there in no time. I turn into the drive-through line, thinking to myself, surely the line should not be long this early in the morning. Damn, there would be a line today out of all days. Should I get out of line while I still can?

"We're next in line," Nicole says with pure excitement in her voice. I guess my question was answered; I wait.

The slight breeze of the early spring morning has settled in. I wish that the weather would stay like this for the rest of the day. Living in the South, I have learned that you do everything in the morning because by noon, the humidity will take your breath away. "May I take your order?" asks the young girl over the speaker.

"Yes, let me have a pink cake donut with sprinkles and a large cup of coffee."

"That will be $4.59 at the next window."

Oh my God, what are these people ordering in front of me? I have been waiting for almost 10 minutes. How many donuts do they need? Don't these people understand that I have to be at work in 45 minutes? And I have to travel across town? Irritated, I turn up the music to drown out my thoughts as my granddaughter sings in the back seat. It must be nice that children do not have a care in the world. At least most children. My mind starts to drift back to when I was a child. I would have never been able to get a donut before going to school, let alone sing my favorite song with the radio.

1 | IT'S A FIRE

As I watch the blood pour down the white bowl in the bathroom, I hold my breath as I try to keep my finger still. Feeling the cold water on the open cut, I look at my mother through the mirror and wonder why she would do this to me?

"Hold still before I give you something to cry about."

I begin to tremble as she raises the switch once again to hit me across my back. I try to hold back the tears, but I can't. I'm only three years old. It seems like forever before the blood would finally stop pouring out of me.

"Go to bed now!" she said.

I follow her through the dimly lit room to the kitchen where my bed is. I try to be as quiet as possible; I don't want her to look back at me. What if she hears me limping on the hardwood floor? What will she do to me? I start to panic because this walk seems like forever. My body aches from the lashes of the switch. So, I walk on my tiptoes, hoping they will quiet my every move.

"Pull out the bed from the wall and get in it. I don't want to hear another word from you." With my small, frail body, I reach as high as I could to unsnap the bed from the wall. Nervous that she would return, I tugged as hard as I could until finally the bed gave in and now lay flat on the floor.

I lay still on my back, thinking about the question that I asked my mom. Are you my mom? It just came out. I don't know why that came to my mind because she is the only mom I know. Why would she not be my mom?

I watched her as she moved throughout the living room, talking on the phone. "Yes, girl, she is the most ungrateful child I had ever laid my eyes on. As good as I have been to her, she had the nerve to ask me some shit like that. She needs to be learning them ABCs. I tried to beat the shit out of her. Yea, I put a bandage on her finger; she'll be alright."

My mom is a brown-skinned chubby lady. When she smiled, you can see her gold tooth in the front of her mouth. I want a gold tooth, I thought to myself. I wonder why she has a gold tooth. Was she born like that? Will I have a gold tooth when I am big?

Mom continues to laugh and talk on the phone with one hand and snack on some chips with the other. I don't see her peeking through the covers, but I can hear her walking in those flat house shoes. She always has on house shoes. She says that she cannot afford to buy herself a pair of shoes because of me. To save the wear and tear of her shoes, she always takes them off at the door.

I looked out the window that was in the kitchen. It's not really a window, but an opening where you can see the next building over. The paint was a dull white color that was slowly chipping away from its foundation. I watch a family of bugs march across the window as if they were going on a family outing. I wonder where they are going. Why do you only come out at night? Do you not want to be around in sight for fear of my mom smashing you too?

I am scared of them, especially when they crawl on me.

"Kill the thing," my mom would say. "It is smaller than you."

I watch the bug family continue to march back and forth. Please do not come near me, I thought to myself. If I scream, she will know that I am awake. I do not want her to know that I am awake; I am scared that she might yell at me or worse.

I start to recite my ABCs in my head. a,b,c,d,e,f,g,h,i,j,k,l,m what is the next letter? I knew it earlier. N! That's what it is n,o,p,q, oh no, this is where I always get stuck. Why do I have to know them anyway? I hate my ABCs. I don't want them. I always get in trouble because of them. Every time I would mess up, mom would hit me with whatever she could get her hands on.

What is the next letter? I start saying them again in my head over and over again, each time I get stuck, so I skip it and move on, x,y,z.

My eyes are getting heavy. I can no longer hear my mom. I think she went to bed. I turn over on my side and begin to drift off to sleep.

What is that I hear? Am I dreaming? I could hear a loud noise coming from the walls. The screeching sound reminds me of a movie that I watched with mom. I could hear people yelling, "Get out of the building!"

What's going on? I thought to myself as I lay still under the covers.

"Penny! Get up! There is a fire!"

Did I hear her right?

"Penny! Get up!"

No, I am not dreaming. I jump out of bed and run towards the front door. Mom told me to never open the door without her telling me to do so. I just stand there and listen to all the commotion on the other side of the door. I felt a strong arm push me to the side.

"Don't just stand there; let's go." My mom pushes the door open.

We stepped out into the narrow dark hall where there were doors of other people's apartments. Should we take the elevator? I could hear my mom talking to herself. The elevator did not work all the time. Sometimes it would get stuck, and the gate would not open. One time, we were on the elevator on our way to the bus to get groceries, and we could not open the gate. By the time we got the gate opened, we had missed the bus and had to walk to the store.

I see people running down the steps to safety.

"Take the steps!" I heard a man scream out. As if he could read my mom's thoughts. Without saying a word, we quickly run down the four flights of steps. I have never seen my mom run so fast. Even if she was trying not to miss the bus, she says that she has a bad back and it hurts her when she walks.

She is dragging me by my arm. "Hurry up," she screams!

My feet go as fast as they can take me out the front door of the apartment complex into the cool night breeze. People are standing around, looking up at the smoke-filled building. "What happened," asks a man in apartment

204? An old lady holding on to her dog for dear life says that someone was cooking and fell asleep.

"Step back!" yelled the man in the firefighter's suit.

Wow, I have never seen a firefighter this close before. I watch as the men race through the front door and up the stairs. The wind starts to blow a little cooler. I begin to shiver because all I have on is my pajamas. I wrap myself with my small arms to stay warm.

Adults continue to talk among themselves as we wait for the all-clear sign to return to our homes. For some reason, I feel the excitement. I don't know why, maybe because I don't get the chance to go outside much. I began to smile to myself; before I knew it, I was laughing out loud. "Stop making that noise," I hear my mom say, squeezing my hand.

Ouch! The pain is back from the whooping I had received earlier. The smile suddenly disappears.

"You can all return to your apartments," says a man with a rusty voice. Everybody started cheering them on, thanking them for putting out the fire.

"Is it safe to go back in?" asks a tall man with a mustache that hung almost in his mouth. "Yes," I hear the firefighter respond. "It was a small kitchen fire because somebody left a pot on the stove. Nothing to worry about. You can go back to your business."

Tenants quickly returned to their apartments. You can hear doors shutting like it was some sort of musical instrument playing its last tune.

"Go back to bed," my mother says as she opens the door.

As I walked past the bathroom, I could still see that the red bloodstains remained splattered in the white porcelain sink. I quickly climbed back in bed and covered myself up. I was thinking about the night's events. My finger began to throb, which reminded me of those stupid ABCs. Now, where was I? A,b,c,d ... until I fell asleep.

2 | NO MORE EGGS

I hated moving. It is so much work having to pack and unpack the same stuff. Plus, we now live on the 17th floor of what I heard was the projects.

"I am glad that I was approved to live here. I don't have to pay much rent," cried my mother with a voice of excitement. She always gets excited when we move to a new place.

The project building was just like the other place we lived in. It also has an elevator, but this time there is no gate attached, just a door that reads out of order. Climbing the stairs to the 17th floor was like going for a hike in the mountains. You had to watch out for things in the dark that may jump out and get you. But it would not be wild animals; it would be homeless people who were hungry and desperate for food.

The apartment had a small living room, kitchen, bathroom, and a bedroom that was just big enough for a bed and a dresser.

"This is home," said my mother walking around singing gospel songs. She loved to sing gospel songs when she was in a good mood,   which was not very often.

Even though my mother did not go to church very often, she would send me with the other neighborhood kids to bible study on the bus. I loved going to bible study because they would serve great snacks. I did not pay much attention to the teacher, merely because I was not interested in what she was talking about. Most times, I did not even remember what she said. Plus, it got me away from her. Her being my mother. I hated being with my mother all day long. Going to bible study was my scapegoat from the misery I endured at home.

"I am going to have Angie keep you for a couple of days. I have some business to take care of."

I knew not to question her whereabouts. I was told that you do not back talk to adults and to stay out of their business.

Angie was my mother's best friend, who lived three floors down in the same projects. Angie is a large black woman who wears short dresses to show off the many creases in her legs. She wore her hair in a short afro with red lipstick bright as cherries in the summertime. Angie has grown children who come around every once in a while. Except for her son, who was always around my mother. I woke up one night to find him on top of her. I was not sure if she was in pain or not, but he continued to come over at night to do the same thing over and over. I would peek through the curtains that divided the room to see if he would get on her again. I would make sure that I was out of sight so they would not catch me watching.

"Here is some cereal for you to eat in the morning for breakfast," said my mother before dashing out the door to who knows where. I was excited because it was Honeycombs, my favorite.

"Eat your cereal," Angie says.

"Where is the milk?" I asked.

"You don't get any milk. Your mother did not leave you with any. I have some powdered milk if you want milk."

I hate powdered milk, so I just sat there with a small amount of cereal in the bowl while she glared at me waiting for a response. Angie continued to make her breakfast, eggs, bacon, toast, and coffee.

"Eat your food and get out of my kitchen." I did not eat again until the next day.

It was almost Christmas before my mother returned. I never had any Christmas presents even though I was now seven years old. Christmas did not mean much to me. I had nothing to look forward to. We had no tree or decorations in the house. It looked the same every

day, dull and dreary.

"Wake up Penny. I have something to show you."

It is Christmas day, and I was not sure what she could possibly be waking me up for. Did I forget to clean the floor or take out the trash? She was good at waking me up and making me do something I had forgotten to do, usually with a switch.

I walked into the living room in anticipation of what I was going to face. Low and behold I saw presents. My heart dropped. I could not believe what I saw. I had Christmas presents! I ran and opened a package and inside was a doll, Baby That Away. I have always wanted a doll like her. I also had new clothes, which were very seldom because most of my clothes came from the Salvation Army or Goodwill. This was the best day of my life. Maybe she does love me, I thought to myself, while holding my new best friend.

I'm going to make my mother breakfast for the doll that she gave me. I do not really know how to cook, but I'm sure that I can cook an egg. I quietly walked into the kitchen and found the only egg in the refrigerator. I pulled out the skillet from under the sink, cracked the egg, and mixed it in the skillet until it was nice and dry. It looks about done. I smiled to myself. I put it on the plate and slowly walked into the bedroom with a huge smile on my face.

"Mom, I made you breakfast."

Slowly she opens her eyes, looks at the plate of eggs. "What in the hell did you do," she screamed? "That was my last egg you wasted. I'm going to beat your ass. Don't you ever touch my food again."

My eyes begin to water. Before I could turn and walk out the door, she was charging at me with a belt. Hitting me everywhere she could. I tried to block the blows from the belt to no success.

"Get out of my face," she screams, "and clean up this mess now." I hurry into the kitchen to clean up the dishes thinking that I will never cook again.

"A rat climbed into the baby's crib and ate the baby's face off." I could hear my mother talking to her friend Angie in the kitchen while drinking coffee. "That is a shame that we have to live in these conditions."

"Where was the mother when the baby was being eaten by rats?"

"In the living room tricking once again with a number of men," whispered my mother when she saw me come into the room.

I had seen rats before but never in my bed. Maybe because we had a dog named King. He was a German Shepard that my mother found abandoned in the ally. King was a large dog that I was kind of scared of but did not show it because I did not want him to bite me. She said that we would keep him for protection. Lots of people had been robbed in the projects and some killed, like the lady who was pushed out the 20th floor window.

King loved to sit in the room with me and lick my face. I would let him because the feeling of his tongue would tickle my cheek, and I would laugh.

"Get your ass up off that floor, letting that dog lick you in the face after he has licked his ass," yelled my mother. King immediately jumped down and ran into the other room.

"Come sit your ass down on the couch and do not move," said my mother.

I quickly did as I was told. I sat on the couch swinging my legs back and forth because I was short enough that they could not reach the floor.

"I am so sick of you," she began to say. "I should have never laid eyes on you," she continues to rant and rave about how she wishes that I was not around.

I begin to drown her out because she has said this to me many times before.

"If you don't follow my rules, you can get out of my house."

For some reason, in my mind, all I heard was get out of my house. I did just that.

Scooting myself to plant my feet firmly on the floor, I find the nerve to lift myself off the couch as if floating on air. I walk out the door. Not knowing at the time, this will be one of many times that I would run away from home. I'm going to go downtown where the rich people stay, I say to myself. I had seen those big houses before when I was on the city bus. I'm going to knock on the door and ask them if I could live with them. I quickly started running down the 17 flights of steps and out into the cool air.

I pick up my pace; I'm free, I'm finally free. I imagine walking to the grandest house on the block. The front door is at least 10 feet tall, with beautiful white pillars layering the freshly manicured lawn. I stand on my tippy toes to reach the doorbell, holding my balance so that I don't fall. The door slowly opens, "Yes," smiles a tall slender woman with open arms.

"Penny! Penny! Stop right now!"

I snap back into reality. A hot sweat broke out on my forehead. What do I do? Do I run to my new house and shut the door? A sting comes across my face. The blow from her hand made my knees weak and I crumbled to the ground.

"Get your ass up! Have you lost your mind? Where the hell do you think you are going?" I look toward the tall buildings through tear-drenched eyes, seeing the lady at the door smiling as she closes the door because no one is there.

3 | THE CITY OF ANGELS

Since we have been living in Los Angeles, my mother seems a bit calmer, happier even. Maybe it's the smog that is so thick at times you can cut it with a knife. I'm not sure how this move will work out for me. I started a new school in the middle of the year, again.

Even though we have been moving around a lot lately, this time, I'm kind of glad that we moved. I get to stay with my favorite aunt in the whole wide world. Actually, we are both staying with my aunt, who is my mother's sister-in-law.

My Aunt Bernardine has a heart of gold. I wish that I could live with her and she raise me like she is raising my cousins.

"Hey y'all kids, come here. I want you to go to the store," says my aunt with a high-pitched voice. If the windows were open, you could hear her a mile away. My aunt was a church-going lady that kept her hair in a bun. She was either reading her bible or watching the news.

My aunt is good with kids; she has been a foster parent for as long as I am alive, maybe even longer. She says that all children should have a warm bed and food to eat even if their parents are out doing their own thing. I have never known my aunt to have a job. I guess it runs in the family; my mother never had a job either. I think my aunt's job is helping children like me to feel loved and wanted. Even though foster kids come and go, they always seem to come back and thank her for raising them, even if it was for a short period of time. My aunt has a type of personality about herself. Everyone loves her.

"Go to the store and get me 6 lemons so I can make some tea. Also, I need a chicken for the soup."

"Bring me back a pack of Viceroy 100's," demanded my mother, shoving 65 cents in my hand.

There is no age limit on buying cigarettes for your parents. I am ten years old and have been buying them since I was eight. My mother says that the price keeps going up. "When they reach $1.00, I'm going to quit smoking," she would say every time she sent me to the store to buy a pack.

"OK," says my cousin Ramisha. Ramisha was one year younger than me but more mature for her age. Maybe because she has friends and people actually like her. She is light-skinned and wears her hair in two long braids that would reach her waist when stretched. My hair was half straight and half curly from a California curl my mother attempted to put in my hair herself. It just never quite had that curl you saw on tv.

"Give me the money, Mom," cried her little brother. "I can hold the money. I won't lose it like Ramisha did the last time." Kevin snatches the money and runs out the front door laughing. "You can't catch me," he squealed. We chase behind him, laughing down the street.

Stopping in her tracks, Ramisha whispers, "Let's stop and get a pickle," motioning for us to follow her to the large bins located in the back of a warehouse. "You scared?"

"I'm not scared," Kevin says, rubbing his hands, "I love pickles."

If I get caught, I'm going to be in so much trouble, is all I could think of.

"Penny, you go first."

"Why do I have to go first? It was your idea."

"If you don't go, I'm not going to play with you anymore."

Ramisha was the kind of child who likes to be the boss and tell everyone else what to do. She thinks she is better than I am because she gets new clothes and gets to go to the movies when she wants. She's right; I do want to be like her. We all do. I remember when she made a foster child eat their own shit from the toilet. I knew then she was nothing to play with.

Fine, I will go. I began walking toward the bin that was filled with pickles. As I drew near the pickles, I could smell the tartness in the air. Glancing around to make sure no one sees me, I quickly approach the bin and grab three pickles. As I turned to run away, I realized that my cousins had left me holding up the pickles.

I darted through the alley, looking back to make sure no one was following me. "Why did you leave me," I demanded, panting like a lost dog.

"We told you to come on," with a sly smirk across their faces.

I hold up the dripping pickles that I so proudly stole.

"You can't eat those pickles," they both say in unison between laughs. "They are not done yet! We tricked you!"

I look at the now squeezed pickles. I bite down on one to taste it. Splat! I spit it out on the ground. It's not ready yet. It tastes like old vinegar. Quenching my face with parched lips, I look at my cousins, who are now busy paying for the chicken and lemons.

"Wait for me," I yell at my cousins. I almost forgot. The cigarettes. "Can I have a pack of viceroy 100's?" I ask the old looking guy with the nappy mustache behind the counter. Without even looking up, he grabs the cigarettes and grumbles, "65 cents." I pay the man and hurriedly run out of the store.

"Wake up it's time to go to school," yelled my mother coming from the kitchen.

I'm already awake, thinking about what the cafeteria will serve for breakfast. My mother never feeds me breakfast on the weekdays; she says that is why they serve breakfast at school so that you can eat there.

Last time I asked her for some breakfast on a school day. My mother started screaming at me about how ungrateful I was for all she has done for me. "Fine," she said, "you want some breakfast? You better eat every bite."

As I watched my mother begin to cook the oatmeal, I could smell an unusual smell. Why does it smell like that, I thought?

She places the hot bowl of oatmeal in front of me and walks away. "You better eat every bit or I'm going to beat your ass for wasting my food."

Looking down at the bowl, I see that the oatmeal is not its usual brown color. It's green! Why is it green? I can feel my mother glaring at me from the other room. I dare not eat it or she will kill me. I scoop up a spoon full of this slimy green concoction that she served me. Looking at it, I automatically begin to get sick. It's rotten! She is feeding me old rotten food! Surely, she knows that the oatmeal is old and no longer any good.

"What is taking you so long?" I'm scared to say anything, so I sit there. "I'm waiting," She begins to search for her belt as if she is looking for a treasure she lost. "Eat that damn food right now," she screams as she is standing over me. Wack, Wack, Wack goes the leather belt attacking wherever it can. Tears are streaming down my face.

"OK," I said between screams. I place the spoonful of oatmeal in my mouth. I can't swallow it. I just can't. It won't go down. Then out of nowhere, she snatches the bowl and slings it in the sink.

"Take your ass to school and you better not be late."

Snapping back into reality from my mother's annoying voice, "Penny, get up now!" I slowly crawl out of bed, placing my feet on the cold floor. I don't hear my cousins getting ready, I thought to myself, as I peed.

My cousins both slept in the same room together. The small room consists of two twin beds and a dresser big enough to store clothes and unwanted candy wrappers. "Move out of my way! That is my pencil!" On and on, you would hear the back and forth from two siblings who have a love-hate relationship. But today, it's different, no noise, only silence coming from the room, I know something is wrong as a chill flows through my body.

"Don't go in the room," says my aunt. "They got the chickenpox, and it is very contagious."

I watched her rub white lotion all over their legs and back that were covered with pink pimples. While my cousins begin to cry in agony for the itch to stop, I think to myself, I want the chickenpox so I would not have to go to school.

I don't hang with anyone at school except for my cousins. Who are now lying in bed drinking lemon tea and being pampered by my aunt. Now I must walk to school by myself.

When we moved from San Francisco to LA, it was right after spring break, which means school was almost over. The school system is different here in LA; I am still in the 5th grade but now in middle school. At least the school is right around the corner from the house. It is a two-story brick building twice the elementary school size I was just attending two weeks ago. Now I have more than one teacher and I still get lost trying to find my classes. I head toward the door buttoning up my pea coat, wishing it was the new fashion waist puff jacket all the kids were wearing.

Well, at least it is clean, and all of the buttons are still in tack. Now I am thinking back on how I got the coat. I'm glad I did not get stuck in the bin. Once again, listening to my cousins, who seem to always be in mischief.

"You know that you can get you some new clothes if you climb in the bin and get them," smiled Ramisha, looking me up and down. It's just like the second-hand store, except you get them for free.

I push the door flap to see inside. There is a musty smell that rushes up my nose. Like when the water from the water fountain misses your mouth and up your nose it goes. It's OK; I'm used to the smell, nothing a little washing powder can't fix.

Looking around the parking lot where the bin is stored, people are going about their business strolling through the parking lot to the nearby storefront stores. No one even notices me standing there in front of the large red bin with "Place Items Here" sign on the front.

I found a crate next to the bin. I stepped on top of the box to have the height to climb in one leg at a time. My feet land on a mountain of clothes and knick-knacks. I did not realize how dark it was in there. I'm scared of the dark, so I place a shoe between the flaps to let the light shine in. Low and behold, I hit the jackpot. There is all type of stuff in this bin.

"Hurry up," demanded my cousin.

I quickly grabbed the first thing I saw and quickly climbed out of the bin.

"Penny! You will be late for school."

Shoot breakfast! I quickly rush out the door and down the street. Walking into the cafeteria, I see that breakfast is still being served. As I grab my tray to be served, I see two girls smiling at me. Why are they looking at me? They do not know me.

"Next," said the cafeteria lady.

What is this? Prunes, I hate prunes. Why on earth would they serve prunes for breakfast? Well, cereal and milk it is.

"Hi," said one of the girls that was just staring at me. "Want to sit with us?"

Why do you want me to sit with you as the questions race through my mind? Hesitating for a brief second, I sit and eat lunch with them. This was not so bad. Maybe this middle school thing won't be as bad as I thought.

After lunch, we go to recess. "Hey," one of the girls says, "let's go to the bathroom."

I really don't have to use the bathroom, but I do what they say because I want to have friends, and maybe they are my friends.

Before I realized it, they were pushing me in the corner.

"What are you doing?"

"Shut up, you ugly bitch," they both say in unison and pinning me down to the ground. "Grab her pants!"

I begin to fight. Well, sort of. I don't know how to fight. Before I realized it, they had pulled my pants all the way down to my ankles.

Laughing at me and singing, "Ugly black girl. Ugly black girl. You better not tell or we gonna beat you up." They both run out of the bathroom like a bat out of hell. I pull my clothes back on my now shaking body and head to class without saying a word. Of course, I got lost looking for my class once again.

Who was going to protect me if I told someone? Who would believe me? My mother always said that I was the biggest liar. Maybe I am, but everything that I have said seems like the truth to me. I don't know what the truth is anymore.

I stop trying to figure which way to get to my class. I pull out the class schedule and everything is so confusing to me. I close my eyes, thinking about the attack. That wasn't the first time I was attacked but in a different way.

My mind wanders back to the cute little puppy that my mom's boyfriend had given her. Mr. Bingley lives next door to us. My mom met him when our house got broken in. Our house was in the middle of the hood and to make matters worse, our backyard faced the alley where winos, pimps, gang members, and prostitutes did their business. Just the week before that, someone had jumped the fence and killed my rabbit.

Mr. Bingley was fair skinned with good hair. That's what my mom calls it when you don't have to press it with the hot comb. I don't have good hair, just hair.

He would come over to our house and spend time with my mom. I was never allowed in the room with them. "This is grown folk's business."

I remember one night, I had the puppy in the room with me. It was my responsibility to feed the puppy when he was hungry. Mom had bought puppy bottles just for him filled with pet milk. She said he is still a baby and needs milk instead of dog food.

The puppy begins to cry late into the night. I was so tired. I could hardly keep my eyes open. Before I could get up, I see my door open and Mr. Bingley comes toward the puppy but stops short of the box. I lie still, pretending to be asleep.

I felt the sheets begin to slide up my leg. I start to shiver, thinking to myself, what is he doing? The puppy is not under my covers. He slowly places his hand on my leg like a snake sneaking up to its prey. He began to rub my leg in a slow upward motion. What do I do? Think Penny! I don't like it! "Hey," I shout, "What are you doing?"

He quickly removes his hand from my leg. "Oh, I was just checking on the puppy," he says, just above a whisper. He quickly kneels toward the box where the puppy lay now fast asleep and rubs his head. He stands and looks at me with a small smirk on his face. He turns away and walks out of the room.

I lay in bed as still as possible, thinking, why would he touch me in that way? I thought back to the time when I saw mom in bed with Angie's son.

I remember trying to focus my eyes, to see exactly what they were doing. I had seen this type of thing before on TV. but never in real life, especially coming from my mother and this young boy that had been in my life for as long as I can remember. I wonder if Angie knows what they are doing. Was her new boyfriend trying to do this to me too?

I looked back down into the box where the puppy lay fast asleep, thinking should I say something to my mom? Would she believe me? Well, I am going to give it a shot in the morning.

I told my mom the next day what had happened. She just stood there and looked at me with a blank dumb look on her face. Not saying a word, she walked away. He never came to our house again.

I slowly walk back home from school to get yet another surprise. "What is going on?"

"We are moving back to San Francisco," screams Ramisha.

"Great!" That was all I have been thinking about.

"Not you, you are staying; we are leaving."

"What? What do you mean?"

"My grandmother thinks that we should move back to San Francisco so we can get better faster."

See, my cousins have asthma really bad. Say the weather is not suitable for their breathing. My heart sank into my soul. Now, what am I going to do? Not only do I have to go to school, but worst of all, I'm back living alone with her.

4 | Daddy's Maybe

I started my period today at school. I did not have any pads to wear and was too ashamed to ask anyone. During recess, I went to the bathroom and grabbed a bunch of toilet tissue to make my own pad. After carefully placing it in my panties, I washed my hands and returned to recess.

I love to play dodgeball, even though I was always hit and was out as soon as the game began. As I was running around, I forgot about the makeshift pad that I had so carefully placed in my panties. I could feel something rising my back. Oh no, it is moving out of place. What do I do? I quickly stood against the wall and tried to move the tissue back to its place in hopes of no one seeing me. But to no avail, the tissue did what it wanted to do and slid down my leg and fell to the ground. All I could see was a soaked filled bloody glob of mess. RING. The bell is ringing; recess is over. I run to line up leaving the pad behind.

I go back to class as if nothing was going on. Soon after, my teacher comes up to me and asks me if I was sick. Why is she asking me if I am sick? Did someone see me? Did they figure out it was mine? I quickly say no and continue with my work. Thinking to myself, I hope that she does not call my mom.

After school, my mom was in the kitchen cooking. "I need some pads," I say without looking up. I hated the way they looked and how I had to wear this large diaper-like thing that they call a pad. However, it is better than tissue.

Mom only took me to the store and bought my first box of pads for me. "You can buy your own pads now. Here is $2.00 and bring me back my change."

"You are not going to go with me?"

"No, I don't have a car anymore and I am not walking to the store," she said without feelings.

My mom had finally gotten a car so we would not have to catch the bus. It was not long after we moved to our new place that it broke down. Now it just sits in the driveway collecting dust and spider webs.

I am glad that the car is broken. The last time I remember sitting in the car, mom threw the TV guide at me and gave me a black eye because she said that I was talking back. I had a black eye for two weeks. Her response after seeing my eye was, "You should not have moved, or I would not have hit you in your eye." There was no need to tell anyone because I had no family or friends anyway.

Across the street lived the perfect family. There was a mom, dad, and three kids. They seem so happy. The kids would always play outside with all the latest toys. Every now and then my mom would let me go across the street and play with them. I usually just sit on the porch and play jacks or cards by myself.

Seeing me walking to the store, I hear one of the girls shout out, "Hey Penny, where are you going?"

"I am going to the store," I shout back.

"Wait up. I will go with you, but I have to take my baby sister with us." I waited outside of her house; I was not allowed inside of anyone's house without mom's permission. Finally, she comes out with her baby sister wrapped in a blanket in a stroller. "O.K. Lets go."

"Let's go to Newberry's. You can get your stuff from there."

"I only need some pads," I say.

"They have pads at Newberry's," Cookie says. "Plus we can get some other stuff."

"I only have $2.00," looking down at my hand.

"We don't have to pay for them; we can just take them," Cookie stated.

"Won't we get caught stealing," I say nervously.

"No, I do it all the time. That's why I take my baby sister with us. The adults will not pay much attention to us if we have a baby."

What a great idea I thought.

"Just follow my lead," she says with her chest out.

She has started getting breast bumps. I find myself staring at them, thinking I want some of them too. Why am I 12 years old and still nothing? Just tall, lanky, and flat chested. That is what the boys in the neighborhood call me.

We entered the store as if we had a million bucks. No one is paying attention to us as we stroll around the store looking at what we could take. Cookie whispers to me, "Just grab one of these purses," that she sees on a rack, "and put what you want inside. We will then put the purse in the stroller and walk out the door."

I quickly did what I was told. I grabbed a purse and started putting all types of nick knacks in the purse .... lip gloss, footie socks, hair accessories, and candy.

I glance over at Cookie and she motions me to leave out the store. We quickly walked out the store and ran down the street to a safe spot so we could check out our stuff. "Hey," I said, "I want one of those pretty bras you have."

"Go get your own," she says. "They are right by the front door." I can stuff the bra with tissue I thought so I can now have some bumps like those that Cookie has.

"I will be right back," I say. Wow, this is easy I thought to myself. I go back into the store and head straight for the bras. I quickly grab two and place them into my purse.

I head for the double doors that led outside when a man approached me and said, "Come with me. I think you have something that belongs to us that you did not pay for." My heart drops. She is going to kill me is all I could think. I begin to cry, as Cookie looks at me through the window and runs down the street with stroller in hand.

The store manager took me home. My mother was standing outside waiting for us. He had already called her, so I knew I was in trouble. "I am not going to take her to jail," said the store manager. "She needs to learn that she cannot take things without paying for them. I hope that she has learned her lesson."

"Go in the house," my mother, screams at me. I brushed past the store manager and my mom and quickly went into my room. Thinking, damn I forgot the pads.

After the store manager left, my mother came into the room going off as expected, talking about how she is so tired of me and my shit. "Go and get me a switch off the tree and it better not be a small one."

I quickly did as I was told. I hand her the switch and she quickly grabs it and places it into water. That is so it will not break when she is hitting me upside my head. The water did not do any good because she continued to beat me until it broke. I had so many whelps I could not count them all.

"I am going to call your father," she screams. "You gotta get out of my house." She continues to rant and rave about how she does not want me anymore. "Pack your shit. You are getting out of my house."

My pleasure I thought to myself. "No," she screams. "Leave all that shit right there. You will go as you came - with nothing."

I have only seen my dad a couple of times even though I knew that he lives here in L.A. My mom did not talk about him very often, just that he was an alcoholic and loved women.

"Let's go," she yells at me. We walked a couple of blocks to a bar and there he was sitting outside drinking on something and talking to a bunch of other men. All this time, he was right around the corner and never bothered to see about me?

"Here is your daughter," she says, giving him a nasty look and walks away. He looked down at me. I could see a small sad smile that came across his face.

"Hi Penny," he said to me. "Do you want a soda?"

"Yes," I say. I followed him into the smoke-filled room where there were old men playing pool or dice, drinking, and flirting with women.

I sit on a stool next to him as he orders us both a drink. He begins to tell me how much he loves me however he could not take care of me and I would have to go back home. He continues to say that he will come and get me when he gets his stuff together. I look down at my bruised arm thinking why me God? I hate my life.

As if she could read his mind or hear our conversation through the loud music playing from the jukebox, I see her enter the bar. "Let's go," she says to me. I slid down the bar stool and walked out the door leaving the unopened soda behind. That would be the last time that I would see my dad alive.

Two months had gone by and everything was back to normal, whatever that means. Go feed the chickens I hear my mom say and after you are done with that, I want you to collect some eggs and sell them to the neighbors.

My mom had a backyard full of chickens. She had made a chicken coop where they could lay their eggs. One of the chickens she let loose in the yard name was Namoni. She was an African chicken that apparently did not like kids. Every time I would go in the yard, she would fluff up her feathers and charge after me.

"Hit the chicken with the rake," my mom would scream "and stop running away from it."

"It is trying to bite me," I would say frantically, as the chicken would chase me around the yard. Leave me alone I would scream at the chicken but to no avail; it would continue to chase me. I got the courage to raise the rake and hit it in the head. It fluffed its wings, looked at me, and came after me again. I once again raised the rake to hit it, but I dropped the rake. I ran as fast as I could back into the house.

"Where are the eggs," my mom says?

"I'm scared," I say.

Ignoring what I had just said, she said, "Get them eggs or get your ass beat."

Slowly I walk back into the yard where I see Namoni standing in a corner like a boxer in the ring waiting for its challenge. I quickly go into the chicken coop and gather as many eggs, as fast as possible. I can see my mom glaring out the kitchen window looking at me to see who was going to win the fight.

"I got them," I squealed with excitement placing them in the used egg cartons. Proud of my accomplishment I walk down the street going from door to door asking if anybody wanted to buy some eggs.

"Penny! Penny!" I heard my mom calling my name. What did I do wrong this time I thought to myself? I am trying to sell the eggs like she said. I now see her looking for me up and down the street. I returned to the house to see what she wanted.

She looks at me and says, "Your dad is dead and we have to go and identify the body."

WHAT? I say to myself. He was supposed to come and get me. Dead! I just look at her. I don't feel anything because I don't know him to have much feeling about him. I notice she has the same look on her face as me, blank. I guess she does not know him either.

I carefully place the eggs on the table and follow her out the door. When we get to the apartment complex where he lives, you could smell the odor of dead flesh. We walk down a narrow dark, dingy hallway until we reach his door. The police were already there waiting for my mom; they are still married, and she is next of kin.

As we entered the apartment, I glanced around the small studio and saw a bunch of pill bottles and empty bottles of alcohol. My eyes moved to the bed where he lay with one arm hanging over the bed dead. The mattress was filthy with sheets that look as if they had not been washed since they were purchased from the store.

"I just found him like that," a skinny woman with unkempt red hair, said to the police. I continue to stare at his dead body.

"Is this your husband," the police ask my mom. "Yes," she says and walks out the door. Just like that, she turns and looks at me, "Pack your stuff. We are moving back to San Francisco."

5 | Like a Virgin

"Penny! Telephone!" Who could possibly be calling me, I think to myself? I pretend not to hear her. As I usually do. My bedroom was a small walk-in closet. No windows, just a small homemade bed made of pallets. A twin bed would have been too big to fit. I could stretch my arms and could touch both sides of the wall. The opposite side of the room was a tiny shelf made for extra clothes. The pole was removed for hanging clothes. I had no need for it anyway. All my clothes fit snug on the shelf.

I sit on the floor crisscross applesauce reading my book. Mom did not allow me to sit on the bed. She says that beds are not for sitting, they are for sleeping only.

"Penny? Do you hear me calling you? I said telephone." I quickly jumped up and placed my book on the bed. I stepped around the corner where I could hear my mother talking to someone on the phone.

"Hold on; here she is."

"Who is it?" I whisper.

"It is your cousin, Grace."

Grace? I don't know a Grace. I grab the telephone receiver and in a low   voice I say, "Hello."

"Hi baby." I hear a woman with a soft kind voice on the other end say to me.

"Hi", I say.

"How are you?"

"I'm fine," I say rubbing my head thinking, why is this woman calling me. My mother is standing over me like a hawk, listening to every word I say. I think that she was trying to hear what Grace was saying to me. She looked kinda nervous, rubbing her hands as if she was on her way to the electric chair. I could see the sweat begin to form on her forehead.

"Do you know that you have sisters and brothers?"

"What you say? I don't understand what you are talking about. I don't have any sisters and brothers."

"Yes you do," she goes on to say.

I blank out, thinking she must have the wrong Penny. I look up at my mother; she has a blank stare on her face. "Penny? Are you there?"

"Yes I am."

"I am going to come visit you in a couple of weeks. OK?"

"OK," I say. Before she could say goodbye, my mother snatches the phone from me and I quickly go back into my room.

I sit on the floor and attempt to listen to the rest of the phone conversation that my mother is having with this woman that I have never seen before.

I could hear her words in my head over and over again. You have sisters and brothers. What is this woman talking about? I am 14 years old. I would know if I had brothers and sisters. My mother said that she could not have any children until I came alone.

I remember asking her one-day why she named me Penny. "I named you Penny because pennies are for good luck. I was going to name you lucky but that seemed like a silly name. I like Penny instead."

I hear my mother walking toward my room. "What did she say to you?"

"Are you my mother," I blurted out?

"What are you talking about?" She looked puzzled by my question.

"Well, Grace says that I have other sisters and brothers."

"Do you see any sisters or brothers? You know that I could not have any other children besides you." Her eyes begin to water as she goes on about how she had so many miscarriages.

"Do you know of any other mother?"

"No," I say quietly, and I lower my head to the floor and stare at an army of ants marching across the floor searching for food.

"I've been good to you. I have sacrificed my whole life for you ... bla bla bla."

I have heard this story a million times. By the time she was finished talking about how she had such a bad life I had forgotten all about the sibling thing. Maybe I misunderstood what she was saying to me. Surely my mother would not lie to me. She always says that she hates a liar and a thief. My mother doesn't lie.

After she had the satisfaction that I was on her side, she walked back into the living room and continued to watch TV, as if the conversation never took place. "Penny, Go to bed!"

"Ten cents," says the bus driver. I quickly reached in my pocket and pulled out two nickels and dropped them into the silver slot on the bus. I had to take the city bus to school, there was no school bus that took me to Balboa High School. It was too far for me to walk. I missed a lot of days of school because my mother did not have the money for me to catch the bus.

I did not care for going to school anyway. We moved around so much, I totally missed middle school except for the few weeks when I lived in L.A. Once again, I am stuck at a school where I have no friends.

I don't think my mother cares if I go to school either. She never pushed the subject, except for the time when she thought the welfare lady was coming to the house to check up on me. She ran around the house like a mad woman hiding the used toaster and coffee pot under the bed. "You can't have fancy things, or the welfare woman will cut you off."

I stepped off the bus into the cool California breeze. Students of all different shades and colors gather around in cliques. The blacks with blacks, the whites with the whites. Not to mention you have Chinese kids not really hanging with anyone just overtaking the school with the different language no one understands but them. Dang! I wish I had some Chinese food right now. They make the best Chinese food in Chinatown.

I walk past a group of boys hanging out on the steps. Like they are at the park scoping out their next victim to run a train on. "Hey, Miss Thang," I hear one of them say. I don't look up to see who was talking to me; I know just who it is.

Just yesterday, I decided to skip class and hang out with Jordan. Jordan was a dark-skinned girl with long hair. Her mother would pay for her to go to the beauty shop once a week and have her hair pressed. One day in math class I asked her if I could go with her. "I don't care," Jordan says, "I could use the company." I wanted to know how it felt to go to the beauty shop. I fantasized that I was the one having my scalp massaged under the warm soapy water. I was the one under the hair dryer. I was the one feeling the curls hang on my shoulders and bounce as I sashayed down the hall for all the boys to see. I knew that would never happen, but I can dream right?

It felt good knowing that she said yes, I could go with her. She must like to hang with me. I don't know why, I don't have any money or nice clothes like she does, but she does not seem to mind.

"First, let's stop off at my boyfriend's house," she squealed with excitement.

"Your boyfriend? I did not know that you had a boyfriend. Shouldn't he be at school like us?"

"Yes, but he told his mom that he was sick and had to stay home." I didn't question her motive, I happily agreed and followed her to the bus stop.

We had to catch two busses and walk five blocks to get to the house where her boyfriend lived. Here we are she said racing up the stairs, me right on her trail. As we neared the front door, I could hear the music playing and a musty smell that seemed to linger around the frame of the door.

We walked into the living room, the lights were turned off, but I could see the silhouette of bodies everywhere and the smell of what I believe was sex in the air. As my eyes adjusted to the light, I could see some of the boys that go to our school. Where did Jordan go? I search around the room with my arms wrapped around my body in fear that someone would attack me. Funny thing, I wished a boy would approach me. I wanted him to. I was still a virgin, but the feeling was there.

I had a boyfriend when I was in LA, but we never made it to second base. He was a gang member of the Crips, but I did not care even though my favorite color is red. I dare not cross that line. You would get jumped in broad daylight if you were caught wearing the wrong color in the wrong neighborhood.

It's something about dark-skinned boys I am attracted to. I think dark-skinned boys are bad boys. At least that is how they betray themselves on TV.

Derek did not live in my neighborhood but a few blocks away. I would sit on the porch and watch him ride his blue PT cruiser up and down the street. I was not allowed to leave the porch unless my mother say that it is OK. But sometimes I would sneak off and run across the street to my friend's house pretending that I am visiting her.

Derek had the whitest teeth and the voice of an innocent little boy even though word on the street was, he was far from innocent. I could not say anything to him, I don't know what to say. I just listen to him crack jokes that I'm not even sure if they are funny or not. "Penny, you want to be my girlfriend?" he says out of nowhere.

"YES," I almost scream at him as he rides around in circles on his bike.

Stopping suddenly in front of me, he gives me a kiss on the lips and rides off. I'm in shock, I just stand in the middle of the street frozen in time until I hear that annoying voice. "Penny! Get in this house! Who told you to leave off the porch?"

I was put on punishment for a month for leaving the porch without permission.

The next time I saw Derek, he was not on his bike he was walking down the street. He wanted to see me; it was important. How could I get away to talk to my boyfriend? Before the thought could leave my head. "Penny. I need for you to go to the store for me." Thank you, God, this is my chance. I quickly grabbed the money and the half-written note with the list of items on it and ran down the street.

As I approach Derek, I see a sad look on his face. I sit next to him on the curb. "What's wrong?" I look puzzled.

He stands up and looks down at me with beady eyes. "You can't be my girlfriend!" "What you say?"

"I can't be your boyfriend." I look at him in disbelief. He goes on to say, "You're too skinny." He looks me up and down then turns and walk off down the street as if he was a stranger passing by, leaving me sitting on the curb looking stupid. That was the last time I saw Derek.

I could hear Jordan's voice drawing closer. I bumped into a bed that was half made. "There you are," looking down at her as she begins to take off her clothes to make out with her boyfriend.

"You can stay if you like. You see all these boys in the room? You can do what you want, I won't tell."

"I thought that we were going to the beauty shop so you can get your hair done?"

"I just said that so you can cover for me."

I sit on the bed next to her as she makes out with her boyfriend. No one is paying me any attention. I slowly stand up and walk out of the house. No one even noticed I was gone.

The next day I am back at school as if nothing had ever happened. "You hear me talking to you bitch!" My heart begins to race. I could hear the two girls standing next to the group of boys snickering and looking at me. What are they talking about I wonder? Did those boys lie on me as if I had slept with them?

I keep walking as fast as my legs could take me to class. Panting, I make it just before the bell rang. I like science class because you get to do cool projects. I plop down on the stool next to a slim framed Chinese girl. She was one of the smartest girls in class. She never said a word to me even though I sat right next to her.

"Alright students get into your groups," I hear the teacher say. I don't have a group because I was absent the day the groups were picked. I just sit on the stool watching other students scramble around talking among themselves about the project that will be due in a week.

I glance down to spot the Chinese girl's purse sitting on the desk. I wonder if she has any money in her purse. I quickly scan the room to see if anyone was watching. I slowly slipped my hand in her purse to unzip the side pocket, and there it was $10 dollars.   Bingo. I quickly slipped the money in my bag and jumped up to join the first group I saw.

Out of nowhere, I hear the Chinese girl scream, "Someone took my money out of my purse!" I wonder who that could have been? I thought with a mischievous look on my face. They will never know it was me, I'm on the other side of the room.

"No one is leaving this classroom until the money shows up," I hear my teacher screaming at the top of her voice. I watch my teacher pick up the phone to get back up from the office. In a blink of an eye, here comes the principal and the school security telling everyone to go back to their seats.

I don't move, the security is now searching everyone's bags. I could hear my heart beating about to pop out of my chest. Don't worry Penny I say to myself; they will never think it is you.

"Whose bag is this?" asks Security, picking it up and pulling out the $10 dollar bill.

"That is Penny's bag," I hear the Chinese girl say. Suddenly it just gets quiet in the class with all eyes on me.

"Penny is this your bag?" I just look at the bag as if I had never seen it before. "Penny, I need you to go to the office." The whole class was as quiet as a church mouse staring at me.

I quickly stood up and walked out of the room. I did not go to the office. I walked straight out the front door of the school.

"Penny!" Who is calling me? "Penny, wait up!" I turned around to see one of my classmates. As a matter of fact, one of the same boys I had seen at the house just yesterday. Stopping in my tracks, I quickly turned to connect the voice with the face. "Dang you walk fast. Where are you going?"

"Home," I say.

"You want to have sex?" I look at him puzzled. Not hi, how was your day? Not even did he ask if he could have the answers to the quiz set for Friday. That is if I'm at school on Friday. When I do go to school, I seem to get all the answers right on any test I take. I don't know how, I never study.

Do you want to have sex is all I hear him say again? Did he just say, do I want to have sex? I scream in my head! I look up at him with a stupid look on my face. Before I could even decide on what to say, my mouth blurted out, "Sure." I don't talk much, but when I do, I speak before I think. I can't back down now, what if he wants to be my boyfriend?

"Let's go over here in the bushes so no one could see us," he says with a sly smirk on his face. I quickly did as I was told and followed him into the tall bushes which faced the freeway. My heart begins to beat fast. My legs started to feel like wet spaghetti noodles. All of a sudden, I kind of blank out.

Before I realized it, my pants were down, and I'm bent over. I could feel him trying to enter me. I stand as still as possible, which is hard to do when you have spaghetti legs until I felt a surge of pain shoot through my body. A type of pain that I had never felt before. "STOP!" I say to him never looking up. He quickly stepped back, pulled his pants up and walked off.

I began to put my clothes on as quickly as possible until I noticed something wet. What is that I think to myself. My curiosity got the best of me, so I put my hands into my panties and out came a red pool of blood. Only thing I could think of was that my mom was going to beat me to death if she found out I had blood in my panties. I quickly pulled them off and threw them in the bushes. I straightened up what was left of my clothes and thinking to myself dang I forgot to ask him his name.

I go straight to the bathroom and close the door. My mom is busy watching soap operas. I take a quick wash up. That's what they call it when you clean your important parts in the bathroom sink. All I could think of was, does she know about what happened today at school? The case of the stolen money. I'm sure that the principal called her. She doesn't work and she is always at home, watching TV and gripping on the phone about how miserable her life is.

There she is standing in the kitchen with an extension cord lying on the table like it was a part of the dinner dishes. She turned and looked at me with eyes of stone. "I tried to raise you right," was all she said before I felt the stinging pain of the extension cord go across my arm. I grab the cord with my left hand and held on for dear life. "Let go of this cord. I'm going to beat the hell out of you." She takes hold of the cord and continues to beat me until she is out of breath.

I stood there in the middle of the living room trembling, thinking to myself, I dare not look down at all the bloody welts that are too many to count. I know it is a lot because my whole-body burns. Sometimes when I got a whopping, I would count and see many scars and bruises I had from one beating to the next.

"I wish I had never laid eyes on you," she would say every time I got into trouble. Until finally she would say, you get out my house since you are grown. I stand there frozen in time. "I'm waiting," she said.

"Fuck it!" my feet say as I walk toward the door..

I'm tired of her threatening me, telling me to get out when she knows I have nowhere to go. She just wants to torment me. I remember when we lived in LA she told me to get out because I went to a house party instead of going to choir rehearsal. I knew I was going to get beat but I didn't care, I wanted to have fun like the other girls at my school. No, I was not formally invited, but I heard the girls talking about a house party in Compton and it was going to be food, drinks, and music. I love to dance, even though I have never been to a dance or party before. I would secretly dance to the radio when my mom went to the store. See, my mom says she is a Christian who does not drink or listen to worldly music anymore. She finally stopped smoking. I wish she had continued to smoke and listen to worldly music. She was friendlier, even a bit kinder to me.

I don't know why I do what I do. All I know is that it is worth the risk. I'm an outsider, just wanting to fit in and I will do whatever it takes to make that happen.

"Get your ass out my house," she screams. I stood at the door, not knowing what to do. I could hear her voice in my head, "get out of my house!" I don't say anything back I just stand at the door afraid to open it. I stood in that position all night. That was one of many times I was taunted to get out of her house.

Snapping back to reality from her loud ass voice. "I'm waiting!" I step out into the warm summer air. For some reason I feel a layer of skin lifting off my shoulder. I don't care if she puts me out. I could hear those words loud and clear in my head. By the time I get to the corner, I hear her calling my name. "Penny! Get your ass back in this house." I stop and turn in her direction. My feet begin to take me back to her. Next time I'm not going to stop, I'm going to keep going.

I returned back to the house and stood at the living room for what seemed like hours. I waited until I could hear snoring from the bedroom and quietly tiptoed to my tiny bed. I lay there looking up at the ceiling, thinking about the day's events. The covers that lay on my skin burn from the open cuts. I deserve it, I know. but I don't care, I just don't care.

6 | TOP OF THE MOUNTAIN

I never returned to school. I don't know if I was suspended, expelled, or what. All I know is that my mother pulled me out. I just never went back. The next thing I know, we are packing up and moving cross-country in a U haul truck. My aunt came down to help drive us to West Virginia. I really don't know my aunt because we stay distant from our relatives.

We pack what little we have and stuffed it into the small truck. "Penny you will sit back here. I made a spot on the couch where you can sit". I lowered my head and climbed into the back of the truck. The door slides close and darkness appears.

I sit still in the back of the truck, listening to the sound of the tires rotating on the pavement. I talk to myself like I always do. Wishing I was someone else, someplace else, anywhere but here.

Finally, after hours of sitting in darkness, we come to a stop. I see the crack of sunlight begin to beam through the cracks of the door. At last, sunlight that was so bright it burned my eyes but welcomed me to its warmth. We are at a rest stop to use the bathroom and eat. I hear her say. I quickly went to the restroom as fast as possible. It seems like I have been holding my pee for hours. Walking past the snacks and drinks throughout the store, I wish I could have something, but I dare not ask. Fill up on pump 6 was all I heard. I lowered my head and walked out of the store.

"Penny here is a sandwich if you want it." I hate potted meat and she knows that. It reminds me of baby poop. and smells like it too. I take it and say, "thank you" because I am hungry. What choice do I have? I place a bit into my mouth and chew like for eternity. I try not to think about it, just swallow I coach myself. I can feel myself begin to gag; don't you do it. The mushy sandwich slowly slides down my throat. I continue the process until it is all gone.

"You can sit up front with us." Did I just hear her say I could come and sit up front? What is the catch? I am jumping up and down inside, I don't want to sit in the dark another day. I climb between my mom and my aunt. I am a bit uncomfortable because there are only two seats. I don't care, I can see the world.

I look out the window and see lots of white folks looking our way. Children running around playing catch with each other and eating ice cream. Why are they looking at us? I think to myself. Surely, they have seen black people before. We slowly drive off and back on the road we go. It's uncomfortable. My aunt starts to complain after a couple of hours. "I could not let them white folks see me put her in the back of the truck," I hear my mother whisper, as if I was not sitting there in the middle.

I stare out the window imagining I am as thin as a sheet of paper. My body begins to ache trying to hold one position for so long. I make a slight move. "Stop all that moving around before you make me crash," mom yells. I stare out the window for the rest of the night without moving.

Day three, I am back in the darkness of the truck. I play games in my head. Pretending I am a princess with long black hair that fall past my waist. I swirled and twirled around and around until I was dizzy and fell to the floor bursting into laughter. Sometimes I pretended to be a flower or even a bird where I could be free and fly away. I wonder how birds survive in the air for so long. What if I died and became a bird? What type of bird would I be? I would be a beautiful bird with colorful wings. My wings would be so long that they would soar through the air with little assistants from the wind guiding me into neverland.

I notice we are no longer moving. The wheels of the truck came to a stop. Are we there I think to myself? After waiting for what seems like an hour, the truck finally opens. "Get out," my mother says.

I look puzzled because we are not at a rest stop. We are on the side of a mountain parked. Looking out into the open, all I could see was giant mountains from as far as the eye can see. "What's going on?"

"We are out of gas and I don't have any more money. Oh Lord, what am I going to do?" My mother begins to cry and bang on the truck.

"Don't worry we will get off the mountain," I hear her sister say in a calm, sweet voice.

Several hours had gone by and the sun was going down for the rest of the day to hide behind the mountains. Out of nowhere a car slows down and pulls up behind us. "Do you folks need any help?"

My mother and aunt rush to the car. "Yes," she said, "if you can take us into town, we can make it from there."

"Sure, hop in," said the little old lady and her husband in unison. We quickly climbed into the back seat of the car and off we went.

"Wake up Penny, we are here." Where is here, I think to myself with half sleepy eyes adjusting to the dark. It was pitch black, all I could see was a house located at the top of the mountain, surrounded by a million stars. I had never seen so many stars in my life. I had read a book once about how there are so many stars in the country versus the city. I guess the book was right. I could count how many stars there are in the sky when I lived in California. I know we are far from California because it looks like the sky has a bad case of the measles.

I grab my bag from the trunk of the car and follow the trail up to the house. Wait! Stopping in my tracks, is this snow I'm looking at? Oh my God this is snow! How exciting, I had never seen snow in real life. I have only seen snow on TV. It doesn't snow where I'm from. Only a dusting had fallen but enough to see in the dark.

I walked into my aunt's cluttered living room that was full of stuff. Pictures were displayed all over the walls of her children growing up. Cluttered and homely, I would call it. What is that in the middle of the kitchen? A bathtub? In the middle of the kitchen where the table should sit? I thought this was only in books. I'm speechless as I glance around the room, I quickly realize that I have not seen a bathroom. Where is the bathroom and what is that smell?

As if she was reading my mind. "Let me show you to the outhouse."

The WHAT? Did she just say what I thought she said?

My aunt continues to talk, "You will need a flashlight at night so you can see the path."

I'm still at the WHAT? I followed her down the narrow path and there stood a small building that looked like a wooden stand-up coffin. She opened the door and all you could see was a hole with a toilet seat covering the opening. A small built-in stand with a roll of toilet tissue.

The smell was so foul, nothing like I had ever smelled before. It was worse than the alleyways in LA.

"If you have to use the bathroom in the middle of the night, we have an emergency bucket in the bedroom you can use." Oh, that explains the smell in the house, remembering the stench that seems to linger on, no matter how good the freshly baked banana bread smell. The piss overpowered everything.

We only stayed at my aunt's house for about one month before we moved to the plantation house on the other side of the mountain. Thank God, because I hated taking a bath in the middle of the kitchen for all to see. I am a teenager, and I don't want people looking at me. That probably explains why I had only taken one bath the whole time I was there. I don't remember my mother taking a bath at all. She did what she calls, hoe baths.

One time my mother made me take a bath at the neighbor's house. The neighbors had indoor plumbing which included running water in the kitchen and bathroom. You could actually flush the toilet and take a bath away from the kitchen. I felt kind of odd going into someone else's bathroom and making it my own as if I lived there. Plus, I liked the boy who stayed in the house. I want him to be my boyfriend, I think he wants me to be his girlfriend. I remember when I met him. He and the neighborhood kids were sliding down the hill on top of plastic bags in the snow.

I watch him as he slides down the hill and runs back up to start the fun all over. "Hi," he said looking at me with big brown eyes. "I'm Kameron and I live in the big house at the bottom of the hill and over there, pointing in the opposite direction, is Tanya's house. He looks toward the girl that is now sliding down the hill. "We are going to go to her house and listen to music. You want to come?"

"Sure," I say. "Wait, I have to ask my mom first," quickly looking down to the ground.

"We will not be too long," my cousin Felisha says. Felisha is the middle child that my aunt has. She is two years older than me and next year we will go to school together.

Tanya has a more modern house with all working components. Moreover, she has both parents living with her just like Kameron does. I don't know what it is like to have two parents in one house. I don't know hardly anybody who has a two-parent household. My aunt in California ran a house full of foster kids that came and went all the time. Seems normal to me. But this is again something I read in a book. Four plates set for the family at the kitchen table. Dinner is served with a tall glass of juice and everybody sitting around talking about how their day went. Wow, I get chills when I think about how it would feel if this was my life.

"Penny! Penny!" Is that my mom I hear calling me all the way from the top of the hill? "Penny!" I quickly ran out of the house and up the hill where my mom was standing.

"Where were you? I've been calling you and calling you. Grab that box and let's go."

Not even noticing, Kameron was right behind me. "Hey I can come with you and help carry the box." From that day on, Kameron was always somewhere near to help.

So of course, he is there to escort me to his bathtub. I slowly follow him down the hill holding on to my towel and a bar of ivory soap for dear life. If I drop my towel and soap, stickers will get on them and they are so hard to pick off.

I walk through the front door and there stands a room full of people. Is this some type of party for the dirty girl that needs to use the neighbor's bathroom to take a bath? I don't give eye contact to anyone. I just quickly brush straight past them to the bathroom. I could feel eyes watching me and voices whispering things I could not make out.

"I will come back and get your clothes once you are in the bathtub," Kameron says.

"I don't want you to get my clothes!" I snapped.

"OK," he said shaken by the tone of my voice. He quickly walks out the bathroom and closes the door. I don't want him to see my tainted panties that I have worn for almost a week. We never got the truck with all our stuff from the side of the mountain. He is going to talk about me and not like me anymore. I ease out of my clothes and climb into the hot water. As if he was listening by the door for my clothes to drop to the floor, he rushed in and grabbed my clothes and back out the door he went. What am I going to do? I was going to put the clothes back on. How long was I going to have to wait in the bathroom?

I sit in the bathtub shaking as if the water was ice cold, holding myself rocking back and forth. How am I going to get past all those people with just a towel wrapped around my body? I hear a knock at the door. "Who is it," I say above a whisper.

"I got you some clean clothes from my sister," I heard Kameron say from the other side of the door. I am so embarrassed by the whole ordeal. Where is my mother? Shouldn't she be the one taking care of my needs?

"OK," I say.

"I will put them on the inside of the door," he says, wanting to protect my privacy. I quickly dress and walk out the door without looking at anyone.

The plantation house, at least this is what I call it because I have never seen a house so big. How did my mother afford to pay for such a big house? This house was two stories all wood flooring with a furnace that you had to shovel coal and wood in the basement to keep the house warm. It also had a stove that required no electricity. This stove also used coal in order to cook food. Never saw such a thing in California.

I know my mother does not own this house because there was this old man who also lives here with us. He stayed in the basement. He never talked, just stayed to himself. I never knew his name and he never knew mines.

I think the house was haunted. You can hear people walking up and down the wooden stairs when no one was there. Squeak, squeak goes the stairs every night as we are sitting in the living room watching TV. "Did you hear that," I say to my mother.

"Yes," she said, "go look and see what it is."

Why do I have to go see what it is I say to myself? I stand and slowly walk to the door and peep around the corner to the steps. Squeak, squeak goes the steps again. I can feel someone staring at me, but no one is there. My heart begins to race and sweat pours down my forehead. I stand there frozen. Maybe it's the dogs. I turn back toward my mother and look down at her feet, to find the dogs busy licking themselves. I glanced back at the steps no one was there but I could still feel them staring at me. I quickly rushed back to the room and sat down.

My mother had found two stray dogs and took them in. I believe she loved dogs more than she loved me. She gave them treats and made sure that they had water and food. She made a spot just for them to be comfortable when they sleep next to her bed. They even had dog clothes. All my clothes were hand me-downs from my cousins or from the thrift store.

The very next night, I heard my mother screaming. I rush out the front door, what is going on? "Someone or something had attacked my dog."

"What happened to Lucky," I asked terrified, as I looked down at the white dog who is now covered in blood.

"I let her out to use the restroom and after about 10 minutes I called her, but she never returned. Who could have done such a horrible thing," she screamed? The funny thing about it was that we were the only people on this side of the hill. The dogs could not get out of the yard.

"Maybe it was the people who walk up and down the stairs every night," I said to her. "Don't be stupid! Ghost can't hurt you."

"So what do you think happened?"

She turns and gives me a dirty look. "Take your ass in the house and don't say another word to me if you are not going to help me." I turn and walk back in the house without saying another word.

I got a job at the fire station cleaning bathrooms and mopping floors about five miles from my house. I found out about the job through my school. They have a program for teens trying to better themselves. I forged my mother's name on the application because for one she can't read and two I knew she would say no.

It was short lived, I quit after I was caught stealing money out of one of the worker's purse. Well, I wasn't actually caught, they just figured out that it was me because I was the only one on shift at that time. It was my mother's birthday and I wanted to buy her something.

Every day on my way home, I would pass by a row of clothing and shoe stores. I would look through the window in what we call window shopping, purchasing whatever I want in my head. What should I buy her with all this money? Slowly walking down the street, not taking my eyes off any of the items in the windows, I clutch the stolen money in my fist to make sure I don't lose one dollar. I am looking for something to catch my eye. There it is. A pair of shoes. I can buy her a brand-new pair of shoes.

"May I help you," a tall white woman said to me, looking me up and down. Like, what are you doing in this store? You don't have any money. Again, she says, "What are you looking for?"

"A size 9, I think. Yes, I need a size 9 in this shoe." It was an open toe sandal, light brown with stripes on the side. I watched the cashier as she placed the sandals in a brown bag, thinking about the lie I was going to tell my mother. I quickly pay for the shoes and grab the shoes and run out the door.

I walked down the street looking back to make sure that no one was following me. No one is following me like the time I got caught trying to steal a pair of sandals out of Pay More Shoe Store. They were actually jellies. They came in all different colors. I wanted the clear ones so I could wear them with anything. As I spotted the jellies, I looked around to make sure no one was looking and quickly took them out the box and put them in my backpack. Out of nowhere a man comes up to me and asks if I needed any help.

"No," I say.

He picks up the empty box. "What about these?" I looked at him in shock, like why are you showing me an empty box? I know why, I took the shoes out of my bag and rushed toward the front door. The man right on my tail. He tries to grab the door to shut it. I must have had the devil looking at him through my eyes. He let go of the door and I escaped but without the jellies.

After several blocks I slowed my pace to calm my nerves. They can just take what I owe from my check, I do get paid tomorrow. Why did I just not wait till tomorrow? Fuck it, I took it and that is that. A grin comes over my face so deep inside my soul I can't hide it. People are looking at me as they pass by. What in the world is she smiling about? She must have a great life is what they are thinking about me. I would think the same thing. Almost walking into a light pole, I quickly snapped back into reality taking the stupid look off my face.

As usual, she is sitting in the living room watching TV. "I bought you something," I say to her, holding out my arm to give her the box of shoes.

"What is it Penny?" glancing up at me.

"I bought you a pair of shoes," removing them from the bag.

"Why would you buy me a pair of shoes?" checking them out from top to bottom. "Next time bring the money home before going to the store to buy anything." I looked up at her and walked out the room.

The next day, I went back to work and gave them the money that I had taken from the woman's purse from the check I would have received. Funny thing is that I never saw her wear the shoes.

7 | THE HOUSE THAT MOM BUILT

"Bring me that pile of wood," my mother says. It's so cold outside, my hands are achy with splinters in my thumbs from carrying long pieces of wood in order to build a house. Yes! We are building a house from the ground up. Who knew my mother knew how to build a house. She had the whole neighborhood helping her, including my boyfriend.

My aunt let her build a house at the bottom of her land. She said that you can build this house and stay here as long as you want. I don't know where she got the money from to buy all this wood because she does not have a job, just the welfare that she gets for me. I guess it doesn't cost that much to build a house.

"All we have to do is build four walls and put down a wood floor." I hear her talking to the neighbors. "Hold this end; hold that end," she would say all day long. This went on for weeks working from sunup to sundown, until finally the house was built. We had to have the house built before winter kicked in.

The house had four walls divided by a curtain to separate the small living room from the one bedroom. It had a small kitchen with no running water. There was no bathroom, we had to use a pot and dump the piss and shit in the woods. There was a cutout for a window with thick clear plastic to keep out the bugs and cold weather, one window for the living room and one window for the kitchen.

We had a propane heater to keep the house warm. "Make sure that you don't get too close to the heater or it will burn you," my mother would say. I would always stand close to the heater because the house felt as if we were standing outside, because there was no proper heating between the walls – just wood and sheetrock.

There was no inside lighting. We had to run a cord from my aunt's house to our house so we could watch TV and to plug up our one lamp that supplied light for the living room and kitchen. We would rotate the lamp from area to area depending on where we needed the light. Most times, I sat in the dark in the small bedroom attempting to read old novels that I found at the thrift store using the small light from the propane heater.

At night, I would sleep on the small couch that my mother found from the thrift store. It was not that comfortable from the wear and tear from years of use, but with the blankets, it at least kept me warm from the cold winter nights.

The winters here are brutal. I would have to walk two miles to the bus stop just to go to school. The snow would reach my knees as I stumbled every step of the way trying to find a low point from the high piles of snow that accumulated throughout the night

Going to work was even more challenging. I got a new job working at Mendy's. I decided to apply for the job when I saw a now-hiring sign posted on the front door one day when I was walking home from school. I had missed the bus again. "I had never worked at a fast-food place before and I don't know how to cook, but I can learn," I told the manager. I got the job anyway. I guess they really needed the help.

"You will be cleaning tables and washing dishes. Can you do that?" asked the manager.   "Yes I can." "Great, you are hired."

I would work three nights a week after school, so my boyfriend could take me home on his bike. Yes, My boyfriend, it is official, Kameron and I are a couple. He did not like for me to walk home in the dark by myself. He says that it is dangerous. There are wild animals in the woods that are looking for their next victim to devour. I'm not afraid to walk by myself, I have been doing it for years. I never had a car, I don't even know how to drive. I can barely ride a bike.

I had taught myself how to ride a bike when we lived in LA. I don't know where the bike came from. All I know is I had a bike. My mother tried to teach me, but she quickly became frustrated with me and gave up. "Hold onto the fence and teach yourself," she said from the front porch. That is exactly what I did. I held on to the chain-linked fence with one hand and scooted with my foot. I never let go of the fence.

"You have to work three weeks before you can get a check," says the manager.

"I was expecting a check today," I said, with tears in my eyes.

"Well, I'm sorry but I cannot push your paperwork through until you give me a social security card."

"I don't have a social security card," I tell the manager.

"Get it from your mother." She doesn't have it either. I asked her for my social security card, and she told me that she lost it and was not going to go downtown to get me another one so I could work at some burger place.

"If you don't come up with the social card, I am going to have to let you go," the manager says to me. "There are dishes to wash so get to it," he says and walks off.

I stood there with a blank look on my face. How am I going to get a social security card? I don't even know what that is or what it looks like.

After returning home from work, I noticed that the house was quiet except for the dog licking her ass. I hated that sound, it made me want to throw up. Where could my mother be? She must be at the top of the hill to visit my aunt. I begin to snoop around the house to look for anything that may look like a social security card. I know, maybe it is in her purse.

Without hesitation, I quickly opened her purse and began searching and at the same time listening for any footsteps that might catch me. My heart is beating a thousand miles a minute, afraid of what she might do to me if she catches me in her purse. She has always told me not to ever go in her purse or she will break every bone in my body. I believe her. One time she twisted my arm so hard I thought that it was broken. It was sore and bruised for a month.

Oh, my God I hear her coming. I quickly put her purse back on the bed and sat on the couch as if nothing was happening. "What are you doing? she said.

"Nothing," I quickly lied looking at the off TV.

"Get in there and wash the dishes," she snarled at me. I quickly did as I was told. I am so nervous that I am trembling. I quickly washed the dishes and went to bed thinking of another plan.

The next day when I went to work, I noticed that all employees would place their coats and purses in a coat closet. My mind started to spin. Maybe someone here has their social security number, and I could use theirs. When no one was looking, I quickly reached in a pocket and came up with nothing. Hanging on a hook were several purses. I pulled out a wallet from someone's purse and opened it to find $20, forgetting the card I needed, I stuffed the money in my pocket and closed the door.

This went on for several days, sneaking in purses taking what I could. I could hear people talking about how someone has been going in the closet stealing money. I just listened as if they were not talking about me. As if, I had nothing to do with the missing money until I kind of got caught red handed.

Right as my shift was ending, I decided to go into the closet to see what I could find. Low and behold, when I went to reach in someone's purse, I could feel someone staring at me. I quickly turned my head to see a worker looking to see what I was doing. We made eye contact, as if I could read her mind. I knew that she knew and was going to tell the manager and I would be fired.

I grabbed my coat and ran out of the restaurant to find my boyfriend waiting to take me home on his bike. I hopped on the handlebars and off we went down the dark dirt road. "Hold onto the handlebars," he says to me. "This road is rocky." As we turned the corner, the tire hit a rock, and everything went bad. The bike flips over and off I go hitting my head on a rock.

I quickly jump to my feet. I am a bit dazed from the shock of the fall. "Are you alright," I hear my boyfriend asking me?

Holding my head, I could feel the blood trickling down my forehead. "I'm OK," I say to him. He picks up the bike that now has a broken tire and we walk the rest of the way home.

"Come to my house first," my boyfriend says. "My mom works at the hospital." I hesitated but I followed his instructions. By this time, my blood had soaked my shirt and I was feeling a bit dizzy. His mother came rushing in to see what the commotion was.

"Somebody go, and get her mother," she shouts. "She needs to go to the hospital." A few minutes later, my mother comes walking through the door, looking at me and the blood-stained shirt, turns and says, "She will be OK."

"No," says my boyfriend's mom, "I think that she should go to the hospital, she might have a concussion."

Looking at me, my mom says, "Why did you not come home first instead of going to her house? You must not be in that bad of shape."

I lower my head and say, "I don't know." "I should not take you anywhere, you ungrateful winch. Plus, I have no way of taking you to the hospital anyway."

"I will take you to the hospital," my boyfriend's mom says. "Just go get in the car."

After arriving at the hospital, the doctor comes to check on me and says that I need four stitches in my head. "That was a pretty bad fall; I'm glad that you came in." I glared up at my mother as she pretended not to see me.

After the procedure, the doctor gave me some medicine to take for the pain. You will have to stay out of school for the next few days and you cannot go to work. Thank God, I said to myself, this would be my excuse never to return to school or work. I hated them both. However, now I have to look at her day in and day out. I do not know which one is the worst, going back to school and work or staying at home with her. Then again, I probably don't have a job anymore anyway.

After a couple of days sitting in the house, I was ready to go back to school, anywhere but here. On Monday, I was back in school.

Sitting in my religion class, which was an elective that I chose so I would not have to take P.E, I heard the teacher talking about a weekend trip to the cabins that included many fun activities.

My teacher passed out the permission field trip forms and the amount that had to be paid prior to going on the trip. $200? I don't have $200 to go on a trip. I never received my paycheck from the job that I was fired from.

Every Friday, we had our weekly football games. I do not like football, but I volunteered to help the cheerleaders and football players sell advertising booklets for $5.00 each. We were given 20 booklets to sell and when they are sold, you are to turn your money in to the coach. After that, you could get in the game free.

Most cheerleaders were lazy and did not want to sell all their books. So, I would go as fast as I could to each car in hopes of selling all my booklets. I would then tell the cheerleaders that I would also help them to sell their booklets as well. This is where the profit kicked in. I would sell all my books and turn in the money, but money from the extra booklets, I kept for myself.

I had only done this once during last week's game. I only have one week to get the money so I can go on the trip. I wonder if I could pull it off.

The next Friday, I sign up for the distribution to pass out booklets. I am handed my 20 booklets and quickly start running through the parking lot like a chicken with its head cut off, asking people if they want to buy a booklet for $5. I made sure that I was polite, and I always smiled at the customer. To my surprise, I sold all my booklets in less than an hour.

I look over and see one of the cheerleaders struggling to sell her booklets. I quickly ran over to her. "I will help you sell them if you like." Without hesitation, she handed me the booklets to sell.

"Great," she says and quickly joins the game that had already started.

Another cheerleader approaches me.

"Can you sell mine too?"

"Sure," I say. She hands me her booklets as well.

I stop to count the extra booklets. Wow! I have enough for the $200 field trip fee plus enough money to get me something to eat. I sell all the booklets and walk home never turning in any of the money.

"My teacher says that we have to go on a fieldtrip, and it is free. I will get extra credit if I go. Can I go?"

"I don't care what you do," she says not taking her eyes off the TV. "I don't have any money or nothing to give you."

"That is OK," I say. My boyfriend had taken some extra blankets from his house so I could have something to keep me warm in the cabins.

The next day I begin my journey to the school with the money I took from the booklets and the blankets my boyfriend had hid for me under the tree by his house. I had one change of clothes that I had in my backpack and some books to read just in case I was bored.

As I approached the school, I could see students and their parents standing around talking about how much fun they were going to have and how much they would miss them. I just stood there by myself wishing I had someone to see me off. That's OK, at least I am going.

I spot my teacher standing with a group of other chaperones looking through the field trip permission forms. I ran over to where she was and gave her my money. "Penny. I did not think you were going to make it, but I am glad you are here. Is your mother here?"

"No." She is sick," I say. I quickly get on the bus before she starts asking me a bunch of questions I didn't want to answer.

I had never been on a fieldtrip before; I wonder what it will be like. I sit by myself next to the window listening to the other kids laugh and talk about all kinds of stuff. They never look my way or invite me into the conversations. I don't blame them; I have nothing to talk about anyway. So, I continue to look out the window watching the cars go by.

We finally made it and its lunchtime. I am glad because I'm starving. I had not eaten all day. The other children had snacks on the bus, but I could not get to a store and I dare not take anything from the house. Thinking about the last time I took food from the house without asking and what happened to me because of it, I'm not that hungry after all.

Even though I was by myself, I had a lot of fun. We had prayer in the morning and different activities throughout the day like horseback riding and swimming in the lake. I did not do either, I am scared of horses and I can't swim. Hell, I don't even own a swimming suit. It was fun watching the other children have a good time.

In the evenings, we would sit around the bon fire and sing songs and the chaperones would read us stories. I loved staring up at the night sky attempting to count as many stars as I could. It was so dark out. It was like sitting under a bed of diamonds.

The last day came too soon, I wish I could live here forever, but I know all good things must come to an end. Back on the bus, I hear the teacher calling the role. "Penny?"

"Here," I say and slowly climb back on the bus with blankets in hand. I wish I could go anywhere but back home.

8 | RUN PENNY! RUN!

Spring is finally here, no more cold snowy days. I wonder why I have not heard from my boyfriend in a couple of days. I walk to his house to see if he is home. Maybe he is sick and needs someone to take care of him. I knock on the door but no answer. Finally, after standing on his porch for ten minutes, he comes to the door. "What do you want?"

I look at him puzzled. "What do you mean what I want," I snap.

"Come in," he says, softening his voice. I see his two brothers on the couch watching TV. They stop and look up at me as if they had never seen me before. "Let's go in the back so we can talk."

"OK," I say. He begins to tell me how the other boys at school are having sex and he wants to have sex too. Thinking to myself, I already did that but OK. He continues to tell me about the plan he has for us to "do it."

"I'm going to take the blankets that I gave you for the field trip and hide them in the woods. I want you to meet me there after school tomorrow."

I say, "OK."

I did as I was told. The next day, I went to the spot that he told me to meet him at. He was there waiting for me with a big grin on his face. The sun was warm and bright. However, my body temperature was like 1000 degrees. Why am I so hot I think to myself as I approach him? What if we get caught?

Like he was reading my mind, "No one will know we are here. No one can see us. Pull down your pants," he says. I quickly, without hesitation, do as I am told. I mean he is my boyfriend, right? I'm practically an adult; I will be 16 soon. I lay on the blanket that I am already familiar with and there he is big and long.

He attempts to go inside me, but it would not fit. After trying several times, he gave up, put his clothes on and walked off leaving me lying there once again, with my pants around my ankles.

The next week we broke up. He told me he had a new girlfriend and did not want to be with me anymore. "Who is your girlfriend," I say trying to hold back the tears?

"Tanya," he says loud and proud. "She knows how to be a good girlfriend," he says to me as he walks back down to her house. I just stand there for what seems like hours. I finally started walking home with my tail between my legs.

I had to pass by Tanya's house to get to my house and low and behold, who do I see? Tanya, my use to be boyfriend, and my cousins, sitting on the porch. When they see me coming, they begin to laugh and whisper things about me. I look at all of them including my cousins in disbelief. I don't say anything, just run pass her house with tears running down my face.

I am so glad when I got home, my mom was not there. I stood in the middle of the room and cried like a baby. "God? Why no one wants me? Why does no one love me?" I ask myself that over and over until my eyes are bloodshot red. I hear my mom coming up the road. I get myself together not wanting her to know what happened. She walks through the door without saying a word. I sit there in silence staring at the TV until it was time to go to bed.

Once a month my mother and aunt would go to the secondhand bread store and by day old bread and snacks. Some of the pies would be a bit smashed and the donuts expired; I didn't care. I love snacks. Occasionally, my mom would bake a cake for the holidays or make bread pudding or what she called a butter roll. I love it when she baked, she was always in a good mood when she baked and didn't mind me eating the baked goods.

I was at my cousins' house waiting for my mom to come back from the bread store. My mom had left her dog there because she did not want it to be home alone. My cousins also had a dog. I watched the dogs as they ran around the house chasing each other's tails.

I hear my mother and aunt walking up the hill carrying the delicious goods. We ran to the bags taking out the baked treats searching for the best-looking ones.

"Which one of these dogs done shit in my house," I hear my aunt say?

We all say in unison, "I don't know."

"Well, somebody better get this shit up right now or no snacks." We all debate back and forth on who was going to pick up the dog shit. I like dogs but I don't want to be picking up shit.

My oldest cousin says, "Let's pull straws and whoever gets the short one has to pick up the shit."

"OK," we agree. She goes to the back and grabs some broom straws off the wooden broom that was in the corner of the kitchen. Placing them in her hand. "You go first Penny." "Ok." I pull the first straw.

"You lose that is the short straw. You have to pick up the shit." I never see the length of the other straws before she throws them in the trash.

All of the cousins laugh at me and dance around the room, "Penny has to pick up dog shit." They rush over to the snacks, pick out all the best ones, and leave me with the shitty ones.

I guess now my mom is a Jehovah's Witness. Every Saturday she goes with my aunt to witness to the people on how to make it into heaven. She has all types of books and pamphlets; she even has a Jehovah's Witness bible.

After coming back from witnessing or whatever you call it, she works in the garden and makes we work in the garden too. I hate working in the garden. I'm scared of bugs. There are a lot of bugs in the dirt and sometimes they sneak up and bite you when you are not looking. Or they sometimes crawl up your legs to find a cool hiding place from the heat.

"Chop that dirt. I told you before I take that hoe and rake you across the head with it," my mother yells at me. She has been in a bad mood lately. And when she is in this kind of mood, it is best to stay quiet and do as you are told. I continue to make rows like she showed me, and she continues to talk shit the whole time. "Do it like this, do it like that." "What are you stupid?" "Do you hear me talking to you?"

"Yes," I say.

She slaps me across my face. "Don't back talk to me." She continues to talk shit; I continue to work as if nothing had happened.

I slowly walk behind her back to the house; I knew that it was going to be a long night. She continues to tell me how ungrateful I am and if I did not want to live here, I can get out.

I'm used to it now. I just stand there in the middle of the living room and watch her pace back and forth across the room talking shit and every once in a while, would hit me with whatever she could get her hands on. I don't even know what I did wrong. I just stand there and take it until she is tired and goes to bed. One day I am going to run away and never come back. Where am I going to go? Anywhere, but here.

I start planning my great escape in my head every day for months. Trying to figure out how I was going to take care of myself. Winter has kicked in and the snow is falling outside. The temperature has dropped, and it is very cold. You can see ice forming around the window seals. I don't care I have to get out of this place. The next time she tells me to leave her house, I'm gone

Sure enough, she is in one of her moods again. She is standing in the kitchen looking at the dishes. "Penny, come here. You see this plate? Rub your finger across this plate. What do you feel?"

I do as I am told. "Grease," I say.

Before I could think, she pulls out a strap and starts beating me with it. I tried to grab the strap but could not. She continued to beat me until she was tired. "Now I want every dish in this house washed. You hear me?"

I say, "Yes," between cries.

I am trembling as I wash the dishes. I think she gets a kick out of torturing me. She starts with how good she has been to me, and she wishes she has never laid eyes on me. She goes on and on. Here it comes; you can get out of my house if you don't want to go by my rules. Bingo there it is. I stand by the door. "What are you waiting for," she snarls at me?

I glance out the window and it is pitch dark beside the white snow shining bright on the ground. She continues to taunt me to get out of her house. I turn and walk out. I didn't even have on a coat, just a long sleeve sweater. I don't care. I would rather freeze to death than to stay in her house another day. I run down the hill. I'm free, I say to myself I'm never going back.

"Penny!" I hear a voice calling my name. Who is calling me? I start to pick up the pace. "Penny, wait up!" Who is calling me? I know the sound of my mom and I know that is not her calling me. And who would be out walking in the cold this late over in the evening? I could hear footsteps coming up behind me faster and faster. I freeze and turn to see who is calling me. "Wait up," says the voice.

Panting for breath, "You did not hear me calling you?" As I adjust my eyes to see who it is, I think to myself I know who it is. It is from school.

"Hi," I say a bit frantic.

"Where are you going," ask Janisha?

"I don't know," I say.

"You want to go to a party?"

"Sure," I have no place else to be and at least I will be out of the cold.

Janisha was a tall slim, brown-skinned girl from my home economics class. She was the popular girl at school and all the boys wanted to be her boyfriend. One time I caught her and her friends in the girls' bathroom smoking cigarettes. "Don't you tell on us," she says to me.

I didn't, as I watch the clouds of smoke find its way out the open window. I just turn and quickly walk out of the bathroom. Maybe this is why she is talking to me today. It pays not to be a tattle tale.

We do small talk as we walk down the street. We really don't know each other that well so we just talk about school. As we get closer to the party, I see crowds of teenagers standing outside on the porch listening to music that is coming from the inside of a house. I have passed this house going to school, I don't know who lives there. Their parents let them have parties in their house?

"Come on," Janisha says. "Let's get our party on." Party? I have never danced before except when I am alone in the bathroom looking at myself in the mirror.

The house is filled with teenagers, booze, and smoke. Wow, this is the life. I should have run away a long time ago. Janisha runs off with her friends and I stand there wondering what to do next. I find a seat on a couch that has been pushed in the corner to make space for the makeshift dance floor. My stomach grumbles, I had not eaten since lunch time at school. I hope no one can hear my stomach through the loud music. I don't know which is louder, the music or my stomach.

Through the dimly lit room, I could see bodies sway back and forth to the beat of the music. I start to rock back and forth too. I noticed a boy staring at me like he knew me. He finally mustered up the courage to approach me. "Hey, you want to dance?" All white teeth. Are people's teeth extra white in the dark because his teeth were super white?

"No thank you," I say, lowering my head and remembering I don't know how to dance. I don't want people laughing at me thinking to myself.

He goes to the next girl. I hear him say, "Hey you want to dance?" The girl quickly obliged. I continue to sit and listen to the music until it stops, and the lights come on. I guess the party's over.

I walk outside to see Janisha talking to a couple of boys. "Hey Penny!" she says, "Come over here. Are you going home," she asks?

"No," I quickly respond.

"I'm going to my boyfriend's house. Do you want to come?" Janisha says as she holds her boyfriend's hand.

"Sure."

She introduces me to his brother Antwon. "Antwon this is Penny, Penny this is Antwon." That is the boy with the white teeth who wanted to dance with me. What a surprise.

We cut through the woods until we reach the Hillside Projects. I have a cousin who lives in these projects. I don't want her to see me or she will tell my mom and I don't want that.

"You can sleep with me," Antwon says, but sleep was not on his mind. Before I knew it, he was taking off my pants and fondling with my small breast. I don't stop him. I don't want to say no. Where am I going to go? What if he puts me out in the snow? I just let him do what he wants. I lay there as he goes in and out of me. I feel nothing, I just lay there until the sun comes up.

A knock on the door, "Hey you got to go," I hear his brother whispering, "Mom is in the kitchen cooking breakfast and she cannot see you here." Janisha and I sneak out the door without getting caught. Come to find out Janisha also lived in the projects so we did not have far to go.

We quickly go into her bedroom and get in the bed as if we had been there the entire night. I love her room, she has pretty flowers on the walls and posters of different singers. A pink lamp sat on a nightstand by her bed with different colors of sheer cloth all round to give the room a feeling of happiness. I lay there pretending that it is my room with the perfect family who loves me.

A knock on the door. "Janisha?" I hear her mother calling.

"Yes mom?" Janisha says, pretending that she was asleep and was awakened by the sound of her mom's voice. Janisha immediately gets up and walks out the room, closing the door behind her.

After what seems like hours, Janisha comes back into the room. "Hey, my mom wants to meet you. I told her that you had nowhere to go and if you could stay with us." I look at her puzzled, not knowing what to say. I follow her into her mom's room.

Janisha's mom was a heavy-set woman with rollers in her hair and a cigarette in her mouth sitting in a smoke-filled room. "Where is your family," she asked me? "Why did you run away? Where is your mother?" It was question after question like on Perry Mason. I felt like I was on trial on the witness stand being questioned about the murder I did not commit.

I answered as best I could. Guilty! I could hear the jury say in my head. Instead, I hear her say, "You can stay here for a while."

I don't know why they are being nice to me. No one has ever been this nice to me before. I walk out of her room and back into Janisha's room feeling a bit of relief. The sun is shining, and the snow has begun to melt. Maybe this is a sign that things are looking up for me. "You can wear some of my old clothes I can't fit anymore," Janisha says when she returns to her room. We were going to take them to the Salvation Army. I know that place too well. I always wondered why people give clothes away.

Janisha gave me some panties with a zipper on the front. This is the fanciest pair of panties I have ever seen. I always had white bloomers to wear. When I had my period, they would always get stained, but I had to wear them anyway. Sure enough, I went into the bathroom, low and behold my period had started. I clean myself up and put on the zipper panties with toilet tissue in the middle for a pad. The toilet paper did not work for long, the blood decided to seep through anyway no matter how much I used. A week later I saw the zipper panties in the trash. Her mother must have found them buried in the laundry when she was doing the wash.

All the snow has melted and it is cold outside, but I stay outside as much as possible. I don't want to be in the way. I hear Janisha yelling my name. "Penny! Your mother is coming, she is looking for you."

I get up and run and hide behind the building watching her and my aunt stopping to talk to people. I guess they are asking if they have seen me. Why is she looking for me? She doesn't want me. Why is she looking and asking about me? This went on for another week, me hiding and running from her. I'm afraid of what she might do to me. I don't want to go back but I know this can't last forever. Sure enough all things come to an end.

"My mother wants you," Janisha says with a weird look on her face. I go into her room, "You have to go Penny! I heard that you have been lying to people saying I am an unfit mother." She goes on and on about what she heard me say. I look in disbelief because I have no idea of what she is talking about. "I need you to leave my house now," her mother says to me. I don't say a word, just walk out the door.

Low and beyond who do I see? My mother. I walked right into her. She looks me up and down. "Do you want to go back to California?"

"Yes!"

9 | SNITCHES GET STITCHES

"You can stay in the house," my Aunt Pat replied. This is the older sister to my Aunt Bernadine. They now both live together in this big house with all the foster children.

"Great," I say. I did not want to stay in the detached garage that was converted to a room with my mother. I followed my aunt upstairs through her room into another bedroom. There were two sets of bunk beds that were already taken by three other foster kids. "You can have the top bunk," Aunt Pat says and walks out.

"Hi," I say to the familiar faces staring at me in the room. Both of my aunts had foster children to come and go throughout the years, but they decided to keep the children that they had raised since they were little. Now they are all in middle and high school. WOW! how time flies. No more, big brother, big sister deal. Now they have girlfriends and boyfriends and school activities to deal with. They have gotten used to being foster kids to the point they don't call themselves foster kids they call each other cousins.

I sit on the bunk bed with just a bag of my belongings. I did not have much, but I wanted to keep what I have. "You can put your things in the top drawer," Crystal says, with a smile. Crystal was a dark-skinned girl with fucked up teeth. She probably has never been to the dentist before. I have only been once myself. I recall catching the bus when I lived in San Francisco all by myself to get my checkup. I had to be about 13 years old. Who lets their daughter go to the dentist by themselves. I know, my mother.

"OK," I say, stuffing my things in the drawer and listening to the radio play Debarge, *All this Love.*

"I love this song," Myesha says singing alone. Myesha is not really a foster kid, she is family. She pretends to hold a mic using a brush. The other girls join in. I don't know the words to the song but by the time we went to sleep, I knew every word. We sang that song well into the night.

It's Saturday morning and I can hear people downstairs talking. I quickly wash my face and go downstairs to see who all is there. My mother is in the kitchen with my aunts drinking coffee. "You can get you a bowl of cereal if you want," Aunt Pat says.

My mother never looks up at me just continues to drink her coffee. I think that she is mad that I did not want to stay in the makeshift house with her. Why on earth would I want to do that, I think to myself. I am just glad that I had the option to choose where I was going to lay my head. Where are all the children, I think to myself? I continue to eat while listening to the adults talk about the latest crimes on the news.

Aunt Pat is the one that controls the house and the foster children. I guess you would say that she is the head of the house. Aunt Pat loves going to church, she goes just about every day. I think she might be the head of the church as well. Aunt Pat is a short chubby lady, not like Aunt Bernadine at all. She is more outspoken and doesn't care who knows it. She yells for one of the foster kids, no particular one, she never calls a name, just whoever would respond first. "Get yourself down here and take out the trash you crazy rams."

"Penny," my mother says, "don't you hear Pat talking to you? Take out the trash!" I do as I was told.

I grab the trash out of the can. This trash can is so large it should already be outside. This is not a house trash can, this is an outside trash can. I guess you would need it because of so many people living in the house. There are seven bedrooms, and every room is full. There are foster children and foster adults that my aunt has claimed throughout the years. Her adult daughter also lives here with her daughter. Damn, this is the house that Jack built. I am used to it just being my mother and I; this is definitely a change in scenery.

Grocery shopping is insane at this house. I went to the grocery store with my aunt. She had so many food stamps, I thought she had robbed the welfare office. Every adult in the house had to give up their food stamps to Aunt Pat. She controlled the food too. We had three grocery baskets full of food. People were looking at us like, "How many people are you feeding," as we pushed the three shopping carts through the checkout line. Aunt Pat did not care about the stares; she proudly took her time counting out book after book of stamps.

Across the street are some boys sitting on the porch. I can tell they are watching me as I help take the groceries in the house. I could feel their eyes following my every move. I don't want to switch my ass, but I can't help it. This is just the way I walk. It's just natural, I guess. One of them whistles at me but I pretend I don't hear them. I smile to myself as I grab as many bags of groceries that I can to carry into the house.

There were also bags of clothes in the back of the car. "Grab those bags too," my aunt says. I hand the bags to my aunt as she sits at the kitchen table dictating to the other children where to put the food. I watch her as she pulls out several pairs of jeans holding them up to measure which child she was going to give them to. It was like we were at the free cheese line waiting to get served, children standing in line, waiting for their name to be called. By the time it got to me, like the cheese, they were all gone. "Sorry, there are no jeans to fit you." I pretended not to care, as I walked off. They were probably from the second-hand store anyway. My mother never looks at me, just pretends to be engaged in the food put away activity.

I walk outside and sit on the porch thinking to myself, this has got to be different. I let the California sun beam down on my legs pretending that I was sunbathing at the beach, lost in thought. "Penny?"

"What," I say snapping out of my fantasy world.

"You want to go to the park," Deante says?

"Sure."

Deante was a foster child that had been with my aunt since he was small. I think he still visits his parents, but I don't know where they are. I never asked why he did not stay with them; he doesn't talk about them very much. Two more cousins join in on the walk doing small talk about school and different activities they are in. "I'm going to win this basketball game," Deante says, as he pretends to put basketballs in an imaginary hoop.

We all start running down the street pretending we are playing basketball all the way to the park. I begin to think to myself; I did not ask my mother if I could go to the park. I don't care. I don't think that she will do anything to me while we are staying at my aunt's house. She waits to do the abuse when no one is looking so she cannot be judged. I have heard my aunts ask her why she whoops me like that. She tells them how unruly I am and how I am out of control.

I watched my cousins play basketball until it was almost dark. I don't know how to play basketball. I have never played before, so I just sat on the sideline and cheered them on. I follow my cousins down the street, but this is not the direction home. "Where are we going," I ask frantically?

"We are going to Latoya's house."

"What," I almost yelled, "I can't stay out after dark."

"Why not," my cousins say in unison.

"It is Saturday. Your mother is going to whoop you?"

I hold my head down without saying a word.

"We are only going to be there a little while. Don't be a chicken," Deante says.

Without thinking, I follow them to Latoya's house. Fuck it, I will be 17 in a couple of months, and soon I will be able to take care of myself. I watched a movie one time about a girl who took her parents to court at the age of 15 so she can be on her own and do what she wants. I'm scared to go to court, be my luck, I would lose the case and my mom would kill me.

After what seemed like hours, the sun was long gone, and the moon followed us as we started our journey back home. "We don't go to the front door because when it gets dark the door is locked and you cannot get in. That's the rule," one of my cousins says.

"How are we going to get into the house?"

"We are going to go through the back door." My cousin says it so calmly, as if they do it all the time. Apparently, they do. We get to the back door and knock on the window.

"Wait a minute," I hear India yell, "I'm doing my hair."

"Hurry up, it's cold out here," Dante says. After a few seconds the door flies open, and we are back safe and warm. Good thing old people go to bed early.

"Get up! It's time to get ready for church," I hear Aunt Pat say. My cousins are up running around looking for socks and stocking and hair bows.

"Have you seen my red dress with the flower on it?"

"Come get your hair combed," I hear my older cousin telling her daughter.

Do this, do that, where is this? where is that? I went to church in spells depending on what religion my mother wants to practice. I guess now she will join the bandwagon with my aunts.

Even though we live in Oakland, the church is in San Francisco. We rode the bus all the way there. It took us a while, but we were still able to stop at Pack in the Box for a dollar jumbo pack with cheese before church started. I'm glad we did; church was all day. The only members were the pastor, his wife, their kids, and us. There were a couple of other people that came by. Not sure if they were members; I think they just came for the food my aunt had cooked in the back. She cooked dinner every Sunday at the church. She also was the choir director, and the foster children were the choir. She was on the missionary board and took the offering in the back to count. I knew she was over the church too, like everything else. The only thing she did not do was preach. And she kinda did that too. I watched my mother shout up and down the isles as if she had the holy ghost speaking in tongues. I think to myself, there is nothing holy about this lady, and what language is she speaking? And who is she talking to? God is probably like who are you fooling with all that hell in you? I sit and watch her put on a show for my aunts. Just last week she was a Jehovah's Witness spreading the good news to the neighbors with pamphlets. Now you are holier than thou running around the holiness church shouting and singing. I am so confused. I think she is too.

Tomorrow I have to start yet another new school in the middle of the year. They put me in the 11th grade because of my age. Say that I don't have enough credits to be a senior. I stay up all night thinking about my first day of school. The school was in walking distance to the house. So at least I don't have to catch the bus or walk to school in the snow. The California weather was always nice and sunny.

I am awakened by the alarm clock that sits on the dresser next to the open window. We all get up fiddling around to get dressed for school. Some cousins were still in middle school, so they walked in a different direction. Of course, my other cousins had left me, so I had to walk to school by myself as usual. That's OK. I'm used to it. My mother has never come with me to school to help me out on the first day like other parents I see. That's OK. I'm used to that too.

I sat in math class; I think it was algebra. I was handed a small book to do math problems in. Students who were in class never looked my way just continuing to work in their math book. I will be glad when this class is over; I don't even like math and have never been very good at it. I stare at the pages as I sit at my desk daydreaming of being somewhere, someone, something else.

The bell rings and it is time to go to the next class. On my way to my class, in which of course I don't know how to find it, I pass by the library. I stop to look at the many different books and subjects. There is one thing I like to do, and that is read. I walk up and down the rows of books searching for nothing in particular. Ring! I hear the bell ring. Dang I am late for class. I don't care. I just stay in the library until the librarian asks me if I had a pass.

"No," I say quickly, leaving the library. I never go to class, as a matter of fact, I leave school all together. Oh well, I will try it again tomorrow. No one will miss me anyway.

Some days I went to school. Some days I didn't. It all depended on how I felt. No one even noticed if I had left the house. I guess no one bothered to pay any attention.

There was a pizza place across the street from school that the kids hang out at. They had the best pizza for $1 each slice. Pizza happens to be my favorite food. I could eat it every day. Unfortunately, I don't have that type of money to buy pizza every day. I just got a new job at the chicken shack around the corner.

I met my new best friend at the pizza place. Here I am, standing in line waiting to buy my slice of pizza. "Hi," she says to me.

I turn to see who it was. "Hi Regina," I turn and smile at her. Regina is in my 7th period class P.E. The class in which both of us are currently skipping. We seemed to hit it off well. We started hanging out every day she even would come over to my house.

Regina had a daughter. She was already three years old. I would watch how the two would love on each other.

I wish I had someone to love me like that too. Even though Regina stayed with her mother, she still had the freedom to come and go as she pleased. Regina also went to modeling school.

One day, Regina asked if I wanted to go with her. "Sure." I say, "I would love to." I have always wanted to be someone famous. At least I can look and watch the making in action.

After going to a couple of practices, her coach noticed me. "Penny, if you want to join our company, you can. I think you will be a great fit." She goes on and on about how there is a fashion show coming up and if I wanted to join, I had to hurry and pay my fee. And my mother had to sign the papers because I am not 18 yet. I was excited until she said that my mother had to sign the papers for me to join. Something about liability.

I stalled as long as I could, still going to practice every day with Regina. "Penny? Do you have your fee? Did your mother sign the authorization form?"

"No," I say, "but I get paid on Saturday and I will give you the money then and have the signed paper."

My mother is in her usual place - in front of the TV. I look at her trying to figure out how to ask her. "What is it Penny?" like she knew I had something to say.

I went on to tell her about the modeling agency and how I wanted to join the company. "You grown; do what you want to do," never taking her eyes off the TV. I place the paper in front of her and walk off. The next day, I see it signed and placed on the table. Great, I'm going to be a star. That dream was short lived, I did not realize that I had to pay every two weeks. Plus trying to get to practice all the way downtown every week was unrealistic. I did not have that type of money. I was only in one modeling show. My modeling career was over.

Even though I did not model with Regina anymore, we became the best of friends. Where you saw Regina, you saw me. We even dated a couple of guys that were in the service. Regina introduced me to her boyfriend's roommate after a weekend pass from the base. He was kind and polite. Not like the guys around here. They are either gang members or drug addicts. But Stanley was not like that at all. I'm not used to this type of guy, but I will play alone.

They were both stationed at the Oakland base not too far from where I lived. He goes on to tell me how he is from Maryland and how he wants to one day be corporal. "What do you want to be?" he asked me. I look at him as if he was speaking a different or foreign language.

"I don't know yet." I never thought about it. The school counselor once told me that I should be a housekeeper, but deep down inside I wanted to be an interior decorator. I loved looking in the magazines at all the beautiful homes and the decor that entertained every part of the house. Including the bathroom. We continue with small talk, talking about nothing much. He is more mature than I am. I am surprised he is even talking to me. He is doing most of the talking, and me the listening.

We sat on the porch, the four of us talking well into the evening. "Hey, do you want to come to our hotel room tomorrow night? We are staying at the Inn." Regina quickly accepts the invite.

Regina looks at me like, I know you are going to say yes. We are best friends. Remember. "Sure," I say. We sit and plan and plot on what lie we are going to tell our mothers in order to spend the night at a hotel. I felt like I was grown. I have never stayed in a hotel before. I know he is going to want to have sex. I don't care. I get to stay at a hotel on a date.

Even though I had never spent the night at Regina's house, I told my mother that she was having a sleepover and I could spend the night. Regina said the same thing to her mother. It all worked out. I packed my bag and off we went to the Inn. Surprisingly, we did not have sex just talked all night. Breakfast in the morning and after that they were gone. I never talked to him again. I guess he did not like me that much after all.

Come to find out my mother knew I was lying; one of my cousins snitched on me. I heard about it the next day. My mother and aunts were in the kitchen talking about how much of a slut I was, sleeping around with every Tom, Dick and Harry. I ignored the comments about me and went on about my day.

"Penny? Regina is at the door."

It's late. I wonder what she wants. "Hey, girl," Regina says to me just above a whisper. I see that she has been crying.

"What is the matter," I say looking at her hold her baby girl in her arms? She begins to tell me how she and her mother had gotten into it and she put her out. Her mom had found out about the Inn, too. Snitches! I know too well about how that feels. "Can Regina spend the night," I ask my aunt?

"Sure," she says. "It's a Saturday."

One night turned into weeks. Before I knew it, my aunt was brainstorming on how to get a check for Regina and her baby. She does have foster kids so this would not be hard to do. I guess her mother said no and before I knew it Regina was gone with her baby. I only saw Regina a couple of times since then. Her mother had moved across town and we lost contact with each other. It would be years later before I would see Regina again.

I'm back alone with no one to talk to. Until I meet a new boy. He did not live in my neighborhood. He lived across town. I met him at school one day. One of the few days that I went to school. I had started going less and less. He wasn't that cute, but he did like me. That's all that mattered to me. He asked for my phone number. Wow; no boy has ever asked me for my phone number! Not even my boyfriend that I had in West Virginia. For one thing we did not have a phone.

James started calling me every day. It was kind of hard talking to him because the phone was in my aunt's room. She would sit there and watch the news and at the same time, eavesdrop on my conversation. We decided that he would come over to my aunt's house. She did not mind, because my other cousins' boyfriends would come over to visit them. One had even spent the night. Not sure if anybody knew it or not. I wasn't going to tell.

I wait on the porch for James to come over. Right across the street lived a father and his two sons. I don't know where their mother is. I had never seen her before. They would always sit on the porch with their girlfriends and other boys in the neighborhood. They knew everybody who lived in the neighborhood. It was like they were a part of the Neighborhood Watch Program. Except they were not watching the neighborhood for good. It was actually the opposite. They were bullies and harassed the weak. I am the weak.

One of the girlfriends wanted to beat me up. I don't know why, she just did. Every day when she would see me, she would taunt me. I'm going to beat you up. She would yell to me across the street. One day she caught me coming home from work. "There she is," she says to her friends. They were all on the porch laughing at me. They just sit there laughing and calling me names. I tried to ignore them and kept walking. Before I knew it, she was chasing me down the street. I lost one of my shoes in the process. She picked my shoe up and threw it in the ally. The next day I found it full of mud. I just left it there as if I did not know who that shoe belongs to. The shoes were old and torn anyway.

After sitting in the sun for what seem like hours, I finally see James walking down the street. I can see the boys across the street staring at me. I try not to give them any eye contact. As James approached the porch, I could hear the boys saying, "Who is that?" The boys in my neighborhood were very territorial. Come to find out, they were all gang members including James. James was from a different gang and the boys across the street knew it.

James and I sit on the porch and talk. We could hear the boys across the street saying slang shit, until we finally went in the house. I could tell he was nervous but didn't want to show it. It was obvious; it was written all over his face. "Don't come back over here again" I hear the boys say in unison to James.

"Ignore them." I say, "You can come over again if you want."

James did try to come over again but not without a fight. Literally! The boys waited until James left my aunt's house and started walking back down the street. He was jumped by four of the boys. They beat him so bad; he lost his shoes too. "Don't you ever come over here on our street again." At the same time looking at me as they toss his shoes back and forth like a football. I know that look, that is a threat not a promise. Never looking back, I watch James run down the street without his shoes like a scalding cat.

A week had passed. I had tried calling James but no answer. His mother would always say he is not home. I guess he did not want anything to do with me or my neighborhood. I don't blame him. I did nothing to protect him. Hell, I can't protect myself. I finally gave up and stopped calling.

One day I saw him at school. "Hi, James," I yelled from across the room. He ignored me as if he had never seen me before. As I get closer, I see him hugged up with another girl. I guess from his neighborhood. I walk right past them as if I had never seen him before. I guess it's best that way.

Even though two of my cousins go to the same school as myself, I always walk home alone. As I approach the corner of where I turn to get on my street, I see one of the boys standing on the corner. I wondered why he was just standing there. This is not a bus stop. Maybe he is waiting for a ride. My gut feeling tells me he is waiting for me. He was the type of guy you did not mess with. He is known for beating people up. He also doesn't mind popping a cap in your ass.

"Hey Penny," he says as I get closer to him. He goes on to tell me how one of their partners was beat up because of me. I stand there dumbfounded, not knowing what he was talking about. He continues to tell me how I had set up their partner to get beat up because of what had happened to James.

"I don't know what you are talking about." I start shaking all over. Before I knew it, he had slapped me so hard I almost hit the ground. I stood there shocked. I could not believe that he hit me in broad daylight. People just drove by without saying a word, as if he was giving me a gentle hug, welcoming me to the neighborhood.

"That nigga better not ever come in our neighborhood again," he says to me and walks off. I slowly follow behind him. There is nowhere for me to turn. No side street or anything. He also lives down the street from my aunt's house so I had to follow behind like a lap dog trying to catch up to its master.

As I approach my aunt's house, it seems as if every hood nigga was sitting on the porch across the street. They don't say anything to me, but just watch me as I go into the house.

"What happened to you," Kayden asks? As if he did not already know. I told him what happened to me.

He just looked at me shaking his head, "I told you not to mess with James, but you did not listen. You cannot date boys that do not live in the neighborhood or else there will be trouble. You better not tell," he warns me. "Snitches get stitches."

"We broke up anyway," I told him as I walked off rubbing my face.

10 | New Addition

"You are listening to the number one radio station in Oakland California WDIR 105.1. Where the station gives you all the latest music and information on your favorite music artist. Get your tickets to the New Edition concert this Friday. Tickets are on sale now."

I wish I could go the concert, but I quit my job at the chicken shack because of sexual harassment. Actually, I was not the one being sexually harassed, but it was going on with other girls that work there. Weston thought all the girls wanted him. The employees and the customers. I guess some of them did. For God's sake he is the manager. He is making the big bucks. At least so I thought. What I do know is that he is making more than me. I only make $4.75 per hour part time.

Weston would always ask me, "Why are you looking so mean?"

"Am I," trying to squeeze out a fake smile. I have heard this many times before. I always have this look on my face like I am mad at the world. I don't know why I have this weary or mean look on my face. I guess what is on the inside shows on the outside. They say, your true colors always show.

Apparently, Weston's colors show too. This was a married man. At least he calls himself married. He really has a white live-in girlfriend with a baby. That wasn't good enough for him, he wanted more. Weston would flirt with the girls, saying inappropriate things to them. Rubbing up against them like, it was an "accident". The girls would never say anything, they did not want to lose their job. Remember where we are from, snitches get stitches. Low and behold one day he met his match. His assistant manager.

MJ was the opposite of Weston. I think he was into church. MJ came from a different store. I think to spy on Weston. He did everything by the book. He even tried to catch me giving away chicken. I am always a step ahead of the game. I knew he would come and check my register to make sure I was not short. I knew how to quickly ring up the order and delete it at the same time with a different total. I did that for anyone I know. I don't care, it wasn't my chicken.

Low and behold, here I am standing in the back dipping raw chicken in the secret batter to fry. Being extra careful to make sure there aren't any excessive batter dripping off the wet chicken. The batter always clogs up the heating elements when the batter separates from the chicken.

"I need you to take a lie detector test," I hear coming from an unfamiliar voice.

"What do I need to take a lie detector for?" Weston says with a not too sure voice. The stranger goes on to say how they have had several complaints at this store regarding inappropriate actions that are happening with the female employees. At that moment, I just stopped in thin air, ear hustling while the batter drips in the hot grease and all over the floor.

"Penny!" I hear Weston calling me from the back. Damn I knew they would be calling on me, they had been interviewing employees all day.

I don't know why my heart is beating a thousand miles a minute, like I am the one fucking with the employees. I still can't figure out why Weston was. Who wants to jeopardize everything for a chicken head? Just a thirsty nigga. I walk to the front of the store, all eyes on me like I was on my way to the electric chair. I threw in a fake smile and that switch I am so famous for, like I had no idea what was going on.

With his appointment calendar open and pen ready, "Penny, we need you to take a lie detector test tomorrow. What time is good for you?"

Thinking to myself, well damn, aren't you even going to ask my permission first. Instead of just telling me what I am going to do? He goes on and on about how important it is for me to take a test so they can figure it all out. I can see Weston burning a hole in the side of my face. Like, if you tell, it's going to be some smoke in the city kind of look. "I have to ask my mother first. I'm 17," I quickly say twiddling my fingers.

"OK," the man says. Call me in the morning and give me the time we can start the process."

Well tomorrow never came, at least not for him. I never went back to work again. What do I look like taking a lie detector test? Hell, they might have found out about some shit I had done. No thank you. And a matter of fact, I stopped eating at the chicken shack, even though I loved their hot apple pies. I had heard that Weston was fired, and his baby momma left him. MJ became manager. Good luck is all I can say. Keep your hands out the chicken batter.

I continue to listen to the radio play all New Edition songs. I guess they are getting everybody pumped up for the concert. I know my cousins are going because I heard them talking about how they were going to the mall to find the hottest outfit. I know exactly what I would wear if I was able to go. I have had my eyes on these two-tone jeans with orange material in the front and jean material on the back. I just know I would be hot in them. I tried them on once when I was window shopping and they fit like a glove. I would also get that cute halter top with the ruffles I saw in High Fashion. This is the store where all the hoochie clothes were bought. If you are looking to impress the boys, this is the store to shop.

Maybe I should ask my mother if she would buy me a ticket. I had never been to a concert before and word at school is, if you miss this concert, you are the lamest. I walk around to the back of the house where my mother is busy doing nothing.

"Hi," I say.

"What is it you want Penny? Just say it!"

I hear myself talking to me, "Don't be scared; just spit it out."

"I was wondering if you could buy me a ticket to the New Edition concert?"

"Where is your money at? You got paid and did not offer me a dime. I don't have any money to get you a ticket. You should have saved your money."

I only worked at the Chicken Shack enough to get two checks. and my last check will be mailed to me in a couple of weeks. Plus, I wanted to have some lunch money like the other kids at school.

She goes on talking about how I was trying to keep up with the Joneses. Who the hell are the Joneses? After 30 minutes of lecture, I gave up and walked out.

I spent the rest of the week thinking about the concert. I feel like Cinderella who had to do all the work for the cousins and could not go to the ball - well concert in my case. Friday is finally here, and I am glad it is. Let the day come and go so we can move on with our lives. I guess I can't miss anything I have never had anyway. But it sure would have been nice to go.

I can hear my aunts talking about me in the kitchen with my mother. "I did not know that Penny did not have a ticket to the concert," I hear Aunt Bernadine say.

"I didn't know Penny wanted to go or not, she never said anything to me about it."

Wow, my mother just lied again, trying to play the victim like I was the evil daughter, and she has done all she could to be good to me.

I walked into the kitchen like I wasn't just listening. "Penny? Did you want to go to the concert," my Aunt Bernadine asked me.

"It's OK," I say, with tears caught in my throat trying to come out. It's so hot and heavy I can barely contain them.

"They sold out," I hear my cousin say. "It's too late anyway."

"You should have said something," Aunt Beradine said.

Thinking to myself, I did. My mother just sat there never saying one word to me. It was also like she was laughing at me. She was glad I could not go. I think my aunts felt sorry for me. They knew I was the only one that was not going.

I watch as my cousins prepare for the concert of the year. You could smell all types of scents, from the burning hair from the curling iron to the cheap perfume that was purchased from the local drug store. They never said a word to me about why I was not going; they knew why. I guess they did not want to rub it in my face.

"Our ride is here," Ramisha says as she uses her hands to smooth out any wrinkles in her tight jeans. Her jeans were so tight, there wasn't any room for her hands to fit inside of the pockets, let alone a wrinkle. I watched my cousins pile into Ramisha's boyfriend's car and off they went without even a goodbye.

The house is quiet except for the news that is always on in my aunt's room and the soft conversations coming from the kitchen. I go to my room and stare at the walls wondering what everyone is doing at the concert. I wonder if they are going to sing my favorite song, of course they are, as I hum the lyrics in my head.

"Penny? Richard is at the door for you." Richard? The boy from across the street? Surely my aunt must have gotten his name mixed up with someone else. Why in the world would he want to see me? And why is he not at the concert? "Penny! Do you hear me calling you?" I walk down the steps thinking, what in the world could he want?

"Hi," he says with a bright and cheerful smile. Damn, he is fine; shit, did I say that out loud? It was like I was frozen in time. His lips are moving but I can't hear anything. Like they do in the movies. I love a good love story, like Cinderella who gets the man all the girls want.

By this time, my mother is walking to the door, standing next to my aunt. I quickly snap back into reality. "I want to know if Penny can come over to my house and watch the basketball game," Richard says without any hesitation. I'm just standing there looking dumbfounded, wondering what type of miracle is this? Yes, he lives across the street and yes, he teases me about how I look or how skinny I am. Hell, he even laughed at me when I got slapped. Maybe he had a change of heart and could see through my clothing to the beauty that was hidden inside.

"Yes," I hear my mother say in unison with my aunt. Everything went so fast. I don't even remember him asking me if I wanted to go. Of course, I want to go. I'm going on a date.

I follow Richard across the street without saying a word. The streets were quiet and dark except for the dimly lit porch light from random houses. I had never been in his house before. Just like the streets, the house was dark except for the TV playing in the living room. Out of the corner of my eye, I could see a body figure sitting on the couch half woke, half sleep like he was high or something.

Adjusting my eyes, I know who that boy is. That is Ramisha's ex-boyfriend. When I first moved here, she made it her business to tell me who she had fucked so to make sure I don't. You are called a hoe of all hoes if you fuck with a boy that your cousin or friend use to fuck with. This oath didn't do me any good, I guess it didn't apply to me. That is the main reason why I am back in California in the first place.

I followed him into his bedroom without saying a word. "Have a seat," he says. I sit on his twin- size bed that was half made. I would get the hell beat out of me if I left my bed looking like this. Richards's room was a typical boy's room, just a bed and a small dresser with clothes hanging out and off-white wall paint with posters on the wall of different girls. In the corner on the floor was a small lamp. I wonder why he has a pallet on the floor. Just a blanket and pillow. Richard sits next to me and without notice starts fumbling with my top.

"What are you doing?" I look at him with stern eyes.

"You know you want to! Why do you think you came over here?" Richard says with a smirk on his face.

"What are you talking about?" I'm looking at the door thinking how I am going to get out of this one.

"Get on the floor and take your clothes off," he says more firmly. Richard grabs my arm and starts snatching my clothes off. I freeze, I don't say anything just stand there as he humiliates me. Through my silent tears I can see a light shining through the closet. Is there someone in the closet, thinking to myself? As if he could hear my voice, the door slowly slides open and a video camera pokes out. Oh My God what is going on?

Before I could think, I am pushed on the floor on top of the blanket that I saw on the floor next to his bed and Richard is inside of me. I just lay there without making a sound as he goes in and out of me for what seems like forever. I can't see anything but the dim light from the video camera. After he is done with me, he calls in sleeping beauty that I saw on the couch. "It's your turn," he says as he throws the cum filled rubber in the trash.

My legs would not allow me to move. Even though I am not tied down, it feels like it. It's like my brain has stopped working. What do I do? Do I scream, run, fight What? I blank out.

I don't know how long the ordeal lasted, or even how I made it back across the street. All I know is that I am sitting on the porch in the cold, in the dark stunned about the night's event. The porch light comes on and the door opens. "Penny, what are you doing outside in the cold?" my aunt asks.

I just look at her and without saying a word walk up to my room. I sit on the bed not knowing what to do. I am so ashamed, no one will believe me. I already know my mother is going to say that it is my fault and that I set myself up for them to do that to me. Why did they do that to me? I lay awake listening to my cousins talk about what a great time they had at the concert and why my life is so fucked up.

A month has passed since the whole ordeal. Every day I have to walk outside to see the niggas who raped me. Is it really called rape when I did not fight back or tell anyone? Maybe I did deserve it. I hate it here; I wish I could just disappear. By this time, I had already stopped going to school, what is the point anyway. Plus, I don't feel good. I have been sick and throwing up every morning, so I just stay in bed and sleep. No one will notice me anyway.

I walk down the street pretending I don't see them niggas on the porch across the street staring and mumbling shit under their breath. I let the warm sun beam on my body and cover me with its rays. I stop at the park and watch the kids play with their parents on the swing. I can hear the kids laughing and saying push, "Me higher." The parents, eager to please their children, do as they are told. That is when it hit me.

What if I am pregnant? I have no idea who the father is. But what I do know is it happened that night. I have not been with anyone else even though my mother says I'm the hoe of Babylon. When was my last period, I started to count back. OMG! I am almost two months late. What am I going to do, as tears stream down my face? I have to tell her.

As usual everyone is home watching TV and gossiping. My mother is in her world singing a gospel song to herself. Under my breath, I say, "Mom."

No response. She continues to sing. "Mom," I say a bit louder!

"What is it Penny?"

"Can you take me to the doctor? I think I might be pregnant?"

"Well, I say" is all she says to me and walks out the door to tell the news to my aunts. I walk in the kitchen and all eyes are on me. I begin to tell them what happened that night across the street. No one says a word just looking dumbfounded as if I was speaking Chinese.

"I guess I can make you a doctor's appointment with Dr. Richmond," my mother says. and that was that.

My aunts and mother continue their conversation about the days gossip as if I was not even standing there.

My mother made me a doctor's appointment for the next day, but she did not go with me. She said that if I am grown enough to have sex and have a baby, I am grown enough to go to the doctor by myself. So that is what I did. I caught the bus all the way downtown every month until I went into labor.

Every time I walk out the house all the kids in the neighborhood will laugh and chant "Who is the daddy?" including my cousins. Everybody knew and nothing was done about it. My mother never called the police or even as much as talked to their parents. But here I am pregnant with a child and I have no idea who the daddy is. I have no job. I have no money. God, I would have done anything to change back the hands of time and just went to the stupid concert. Or better yet just stayed my ass in the room and never answered the door.

EPILOGUE | I SEE DOLLAR SIGNS

I'm sitting on the edge of the bed waiting for my husband to come home with dinner. He always bought dinner every Friday. Usually, it is a bucket of chicken or Chinese food. Either way, I don't have to cook for five kids tonight. I pick at my manicured nails thinking what a great job she did. I wish I could save some money and do them myself. But who has time to do their own nails? I'm already in college working on my degree and I work a full-time job at the baby's daycare center. Not including every five minutes one of my kids are busting in my room wanting something from me. Hell, I deserve to pamper myself; shit I should have gotten my feet done too.

I start flipping through the TV channels looking for something to catch my attention. Thank God for cable, you can watch almost anything. Too bad it's getting turned off if I don't pay it by Friday. I pay most, well, all of the bills because my husband is too busy doing him. The Maury Povich show. I love this show, no one seems to know who their baby daddy is. How funny is that. They get on TV and make a fool of themselves. It's funny to me, especially when the mother is sure she knows but the verdict comes out as a different story. "You are not the baby's daddy"

Ooohhs and Ahhhhs coming from the audience to boost TV rating. Where do they find these people?

"Mom! Telephone." I did not hear the phone ring. I never know where it is located from one minute to the next. I'm surprised it rung because it is never on the charger, always dead. "Hello," I say through the receiver.

"Hi."

It's Aunt Bernadine. "I haven't talked to you in a while. How are you?"

"Fine," she says. I can hear sadness through the line.

"What is wrong?"

"Your Uncle passed today. I just wanted to let you know."

"Uncle Hendel?"

"Yes, he passed last night."

"I am so sorry to hear that. I know he has been sick for quite some time." Uncle Hendel is the oldest sibling to my aunts. Uncle Hendel lived in the bay area in a big house. He was married but had no kids. I always wondered why he never had children. I guess kids are not for everyone.

"His funeral will be next week," my aunt goes on to say. "I know you might not be able to make it, but I will send you an obituary in the mail."

I thank my aunt and hang up. Wow, his wife must be devastated. They have been married as long as I can remember. I walk into the den where the kids are busy doing them. I look at them and think to myself, how lucky I am to have someone to love me. They look up at me and smile and continue with their business.

Damn is that the phone ringing again? "Hello?" I say.

"Hi cousin." It's my cousin Mooki on the phone. She never calls me. What in the world could she want? I already know that Uncle Hendel is dead.

"Hi," I say back.

She goes on to tell me that Uncle Hendel is dead and all the details that goes with the funeral. She starts to tell me about his life. Why is she telling me this? I know Uncle Hendel. I remember when one Christmas he gave me a pair of socks. I was so happy that he thought about me. That was the only thing I got for Christmas that year. I have not gotten anything since I was a little girl living in the projects with my mom.

"Penny, are you listening?"

"Yes," I say.

She continues telling me how Uncle Hendel had life insurance and he was giving most of his money to his brothers' children. My ears perk up.

"What does that mean," I ask her? I know that he only had two brothers, and both are dead. One of them is my daddy.

"It means nothing to you," Mookie says.

"What do you mean?" It means that the money only goes to Uncle Hendel's brothers' children and you are not one of them.

"What are you talking about?"

She continues to say that the lawyer found out that you are not his daughter is all I'm saying. "You were adopted!"

"What in the world you are talking about?"

"Your parents are not your parents."

"What did you just say?"

"You heard me; you will not be getting any money because you are not Uncle Antis' daughter. You are not blood. It only applies to blood relatives." Phone goes dead. I sit there with the phone up to my ear with silence on the other end.

This is the second time Mookie has said something to me about my parents not being my parents. I remember getting into it with Mookie right after I had my first baby. I had already let my mom take him with her to Virginia so I can get my shit together. At least that is what I was told. I did not want to give my baby to my mom but when you are a teenager yourself you don't have much of a choice, especially when the welfare is involved.

I was pressured into giving him to her. I did not want to do it, but I had to. My aunt said to do the right thing by my mother. "Your mother will not have any income if you don't let her take him." She goes on to say how she will basically be homeless. "She is too young for social security and too old to get a job with no experience. She cannot survive without him." So what do I do? I be a good daughter and let her take my son.

"That's why you were adopted, and you are not family!" Mookie yells this at me in the middle of the street. I look at her stunned. She tells me how she wants me out of her mom's house and how I was not wanted. I brushed past her and grabbed what little I had making sure I packed the outfit I had made for my baby when I was going to the school for pregnant girls. For some reason it was left behind after my mom left with him.

"Mom. Tell Nisha to give me the remote."

"What is going on," I yell at my kids! "Get the fuck out of my room and leave me alone I yell back."

The sun had gone down, and darkness was appearing in my room. What in the world is taking Mack so long with the food? These kids are getting on my nerves with all that yelling and shit. It would be three days before Mack came home but with no chicken or Chinese food.

I now sit in the pitch-dark room, remembering the day my mom took my son across the world. She looked at me with sad eyes. "Penny, I have something to tell you." I stand there waiting for what she has to say. She pauses and say I will tell you later. She turns and walks away never looking back with my baby in her arms. Later never came. Now I know what she wanted to tell me.

Made in the USA
Columbia, SC
30 April 2021